Glencoe Geometry

Integration
Applications
Connections

Practice Masters

GLENCOE
McGraw-Hill

New York, New York   Columbus, Ohio   Woodland Hills, California   Peoria, Illinois

Glencoe/McGraw-Hill

A Division of The McGraw-Hill Companies

Send all inquiries to:
Glencoe/McGraw-Hill
936 Eastwind Drive
Westerville, OH 43081-3374

Geometry
Practice Masters

ISBN: 0-02-825286-1

3 4 5 6 7 8 9 10   066   04 03 02 01 00 99 98

Contents

Lesson	Title	Page
1-1	**Integration: Algebra**	
	The Coordinate Plane	1
1-2	Points, Lines, and Planes	2
1-3	**Integration: Algebra**	
	Using Formulas	3
1-4	Measuring Segments	4
1-5	Midpoints and Segment Congruence	5
1-6	Exploring Angles	6
1-7	Angle Relationships	7
2-1	Inductive Reasoning and Conjecturing	8
2-2	If-Then Statements and Postulates	9
2-3	Deductive Reasoning	10
2-4	**Integration: Algebra**	
	Using Proof in Algebra	11
2-5	Verifying Segment Relationships	12
2-6	Verifying Angle Relationships	13
3-1	Parallel Lines and Transversals	14
3-2	Angles and Parallel Lines	15
3-3	**Integration: Algebra**	
	Slopes of Lines	16
3-4	Proving Lines Parallel	17
3-5	Parallels and Distance	18
3-6	**Integration: Non-Euclidean Geometry**	
	Spherical Geometry	19
4-1	Classifying Triangles	20
4-2	Measuring Angles in Triangles	21
4-3	Exploring Congruent Triangles	22
4-4	Proving Triangles Congruent	23
4-5	More Congruent Triangles	24
4-6	Analyzing Isosceles Triangles	25
5-1	Special Segments in Triangles	26
5-2	Right Triangles	27
5-3	Indirect Proof and Inequalities	28
5-4	Inequalities for Sides and Angles of a Triangle	29
5-5	The Triangle Inequality	30
5-6	Inequalities Involving Two Triangles	31
6-1	Parallelograms	32
6-2	Tests for Parallelograms	33
6-3	Rectangles	34
6-4	Squares and Rhombi	35
6-5	Trapezoids	36
7-1	**Integration: Algebra**	
	Using Proportions	37
7-2	Exploring Similar Polygons	38
7-3	Identifying Similar Triangles	39
7-4	Parallel Lines and Proportional Parts	40
7-5	Parts of Similar Triangles	41
7-6	Fractals and Self-Similarity	42
8-1	Geometric Mean and the Pythagorean Theorem	43
8-2	Special Right Triangles	44
8-3	**Integration: Trigonometry**	
	Ratios in Right Triangles	45
8-4	Angles of Elevation and Depression	46
8-5	Using the Law of Sines	47
8-6	Using the Law of Cosines	48
9-1	Exploring Circles	49
9-2	Angles and Arcs	50
9-3	Arcs and Chords	51
9-4	Inscribed Angles	52
9-5	Tangents	53
9-6	Secants, Tangents, and Angle Measures	54
9-7	Special Segments in a Circle	55
9-8	**Integration: Algebra**	
	Equations of Circles	56
10-1	Polygons	57
10-2	Tessellations	58
10-3	Area of Parallelograms	59
10-4	Area of Triangles, Rhombi, and Trapezoids	60
10-5	Area of Regular Polygons and Circles	61
10-6	**Integration: Probability**	
	Geometric Probability	62
10-7	**Integration: Graph Theory**	
	Polygons as Networks	63
11-1	Exploring Three-Dimensional Figures	64
11-2	Nets and Surface Areas	65
11-3	Surface Area of Prisms and Cylinders	66
11-4	Surface Area of Pyramids and Cones	67
11-5	Volume of Prisms and Cylinders	68
11-6	Volume of Pyramids and Cones	69
11-7	Surface Area and Volume of Spheres	70
11-8	Congruent and Similar Solids	71
12-1	**Integration: Algebra**	
	Graphing Linear Equations	72
12-2	**Integration: Algebra**	
	Writing Equations of Lines	73
12-3	**Integration: Algebra and Statistics**	
	Scatter Plots and Slope	74
12-4	Coordinate Proof	75
12-5	Vectors	76
12-6	Coordinates in Space	77
13-1	What Is Locus?	78
13-2	Locus and Systems of Linear Equations	79
13-3	Intersection of Loci	80
13-4	Mappings	81
13-5	Reflections	82
13-6	Translations	83
13-7	Rotations	84
13-8	Dilations	85

NAME_____ DATE _____

Practice

Student Edition
Pages 6–11

Integration: Algebra
The Coordinate Plane

Graph each point on the coordinate plane at the right.

1. $A(3, -5)$

2. $B(5, 0)$

3. $C(-2, -1)$

4. $D(0, -6)$

5. $E(4, 3)$

6. $F(-4, 3)$

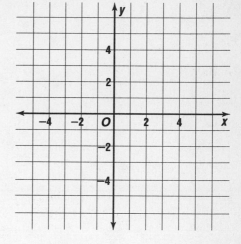

In the figure at right, all of the segments lie on the gridlines of a coordinate plane. Determine the ordered pair that represents each point.

7. J

8. G

9. B

10. N

11. F

12. E

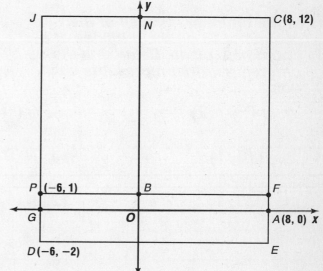

Points G (1, -1) and H (3, 3) lie on the graph of y = 2x − 3. Determine whether the each point is collinear with G and H.

13. $I(0, -3)$

14. $J(2, 1)$

15. $K(-3, -8)$

16. $L(5, 7)$

17. $M(10, 16)$

18. $N(25, 48)$

19. $P(-10, -23)$

20. $Q(-35, -67)$

NAME_____ DATE _____

Practice

Integration: Algebra
The Coordinate Plane

Graph each point on the coordinate plane at the right.

1. $A(3, -5)$

2. $B(5, 0)$

3. $C(-2, -1)$

4. $D(0, -6)$

5. $E(4, 3)$

6. $F(-4, 3)$

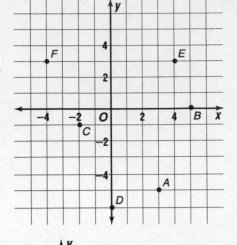

In the figure at right, all of the segments lie on the gridlines of a coordinate plane. Determine the ordered pair that represents each point.

7. J **(−6, 12)**

8. G **(−6, 0)**

9. B **(0, 1)**

10. N **(0, 12)**

11. F **(8, 1)**

12. E **(8, −2)**

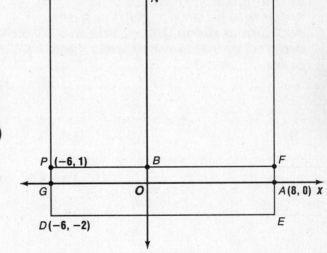

Points G (1, −1) and H (3, 3) lie on the graph of $y = 2x - 3$. Determine whether the each point is collinear with G and H.

13. $I(0, -3)$ **yes**

14. $J(2, 1)$ **yes**

15. $K(-3, -8)$ **no**

16. $L(5, 7)$ **yes**

17. $M(10, 16)$ **no**

18. $N(25, 48)$ **no**

19. $P(-10, -23)$ **yes**

20. $Q(-35, -67)$ **no**

Geometry

NAME_____ DATE _____

Practice

Points, Lines, and Planes

Draw and label a figure for each relationship.

1. Lines ℓ, m and j intersect at P.

2. Plane $\mathcal{N}$ contains line ℓ.

3. Points A, B, C, and D are noncollinear.

4. Points A, B, C, and D are noncoplanar.

Refer to the figure at the right to answer each question.

5. Are points H, M, I, and J coplanar?

6. How many planes are shown?

7. Name the intersection of planes ABG and CHG.

8. Name the intersection of plane ABC and $\overleftrightarrow{HL}$.

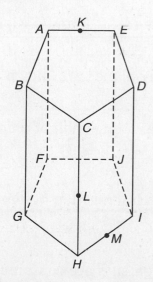

9. Which segments are contained in all three of the planes GFH, CDI, and EDI?

10. List the Possibilities Tim can choose from a tan shirt, a blue shirt, and a green shirt. He can choose from black slacks or blue jeans. He can choose from a windbreaker, a sweatshirt, or a jacket. How many different outfits can he wear if he will not wear the sweatshirt with the black slacks?

NAME_____ DATE _____

Practice

Points, Lines, and Planes

Draw and label a figure for each relationship. Typical answers are given.

1. Lines ℓ, m and j intersect at P.

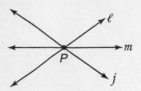

2. Plane $\mathcal{N}$ contains line ℓ.

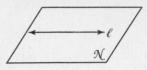

3. Points A, B, C, and D are noncollinear.

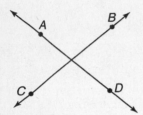

4. Points A, B, C, and D are noncoplanar.

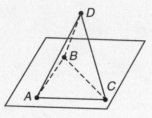

Refer to the figure at the right to answer each question.

5. Are points H, M, I, and J coplanar? **yes**

6. How many planes are shown? **7**

7. Name the intersection of planes ABG and CHG. **BG**

8. Name the intersection of plane ABC and $\overleftrightarrow{HL}$. **C**

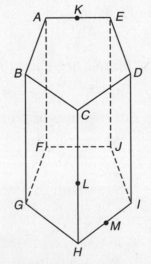

9. Which segments are contained in all three of the planes GFH, CDI, and EDI? **none**

10. List the Possibilities   Tim can choose from a tan shirt, a blue shirt, and a green shirt. He can choose from black slacks or blue jeans. He can choose from a windbreaker, a sweatshirt, or a jacket. How many different outfits can he wear if he will not wear the sweatshirt with the black slacks? **15**

Geometry

Practice

Integration: Algebra
Using Formulas

Find the perimeter and area of each rectangle.

1.

3 in.

8 in.

2.

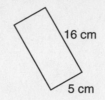

16 cm

5 cm

3.

18.3 mi

4.7 mi

Find the missing measure in each formula.

4. $\ell = 4$, $w = 2$, $P = \underline{?}$

5. $A = 32$, $w = 6.25$, $\ell = \underline{?}$

6. $P = 27$, $\ell = 8$, $w = \underline{?}$

7. $\ell = 3\frac{1}{2}$, $A = 5\frac{1}{4}$, $w = \underline{?}$

8. $w = 7$, $\ell = 12$, $P = \underline{?}$

9. $w = 15.5$, $P = 81$, $\ell = \underline{?}$

Find the maximum area for the given perimeter of a rectangle.
State the length and width of the rectangle.

10. 25 mm

11. 18 yards

12. 42 cm

Practice

Integration: Algebra
Using Formulas

Find the perimeter and area of each rectangle.

1.

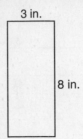

3 in.

8 in.

22 in., 24 in²

2.

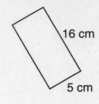

16 cm

5 cm

42 cm, 80 cm²

3.

18.3 mi

4.7 mi

46 mi, 86.01 mi²

Find the missing measure in each formula.

4. $\ell = 4$, $w = 2$, $P = \underline{?}$ **12**

5. $A = 32$, $w = 6.25$, $\ell = \underline{?}$ **5.12**

6. $P = 27$, $\ell = 8$, $w = \underline{?}$ **5.5**

7. $\ell = 3\frac{1}{2}$, $A = 5\frac{1}{4}$, $w = \underline{?}$ **$1\frac{1}{2}$**

8. $w = 7$, $\ell = 12$, $P = \underline{?}$ **38**

9. $w = 15.5$, $P = 81$, $\ell = \underline{?}$ **25**

Find the maximum area for the given perimeter of a rectangle.
State the length and width of the rectangle.

10. 25 mm
39 mm², 6.5 mm, 6 mm

11. 18 yards
20 yd², 5 yd, 4 yd

12. 42 cm
110 m², 11 m, 10 m

Practice

Measuring Segments

Given that B is between A and C, find each missing measure.

1. $AB = 5.3$, $BC = \underline{?}$, $AC = 6.7$

2. $AB = 21$, $BC = 4.3$, $AC = \underline{?}$

3. $AB = \underline{?}$, $BC = 18.9$, $AC = 23$

4. $AB = 6\frac{3}{4}$, $BC = \underline{?}$, $AC = 10$

If B is between A and C, find the value of x and the measure of BC.

5. $AB = 3x$, $BC = 5x$, $AC = 8$

6. $AB = 3(x + 7)$, $BC = 2(x - 3)$, $AC = 50$

Refer to the coordinate plane at the right to find each measure. Round your answers to the nearest hundredth.

7. AB

8. BD

9. AE

10. CE

11. AD

12. BE

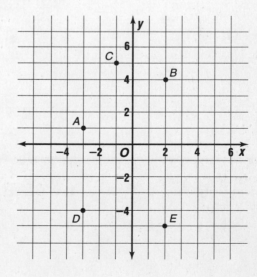

Measuring Segments

Given that B is between A and C, find each missing measure.

1. $AB = 5.3$, $BC = \underline{\ ?\ }$, $AC = 6.7$ **1.4**

2. $AB = 21$, $BC = 4.3$, $AC = \underline{\ ?\ }$ **25.3**

3. $AB = \underline{\ ?\ }$, $BC = 18.9$, $AC = 23$ **4.1**

4. $AB = 6\frac{3}{4}$, $BC = \underline{\ ?\ }$, $AC = 10$ **$3\frac{1}{4}$**

If B is between A and C, find the value of x and the measure of BC.

5. $AB = 3x$, $BC = 5x$, $AC = 8$ **1, 5**

6. $AB = 3(x + 7)$, $BC = 2(x - 3)$, $AC = 50$ **7, 8**

Refer to the coordinate plane at the right to find each measure. Round your answers to the nearest hundredth.

7. AB **5.83**

8. BD **9.43**

9. AE **7.81**

10. CE **10.44**

11. AD **5**

12. BE **9**

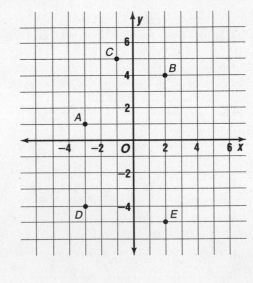

Practice

Midpoints and Segment Congruence

Refer to the figure below for Exercises 1–8 to determine
whether each statement is true or false.

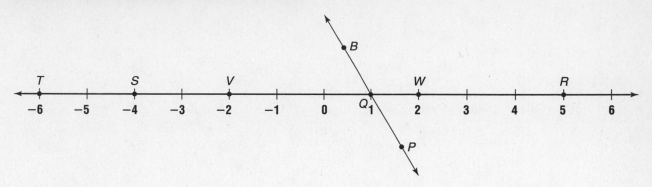

1. $\overline{PB}$ bisects $\overline{RS}$.

2. S is the midpoint of $\overline{TV}$.

3. $\overline{SV} \cong \overline{TS}$

4. V is the midpoint of $\overline{TW}$.

5. W bisects $\overline{VR}$.

6. $\overline{WR} \cong \overline{QV}$

7. $\overline{SW}$ is longer than $\overline{VR}$.

8. $VW \leq TV$

Given the coordinate of one endpoint of $\overline{AB}$ and its midpoint M, find the coordinates of the other endpoint.

9. $A(0, 9), M(2, 5)$

10. $B(-5, 1), M(1, -1)$

11. $A(-2, 3)\ M(0.5, 0.5)$

12. $A(4, 2), M(-2, 10)$

In the figure at the right, $\overline{WY}$ bisects $\overline{UV}$ at Y and $\overline{UY}$ bisects TW at X. For each situation, find the value of x and the measure of the indicated segment.

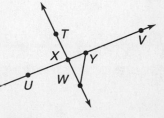

13. $UY = 4x - 3, YV = x;\ UV$

14. $UV = x + 6, UY = x - 1;\ YV$

15. $TX = 2x + 1, XW = x + 7;\ TW$

16. $WX = x + 5, TW = 4x + 5:\ TX$

Practice

Midpoints and Segment Congruence

Refer to the figure below for Exercises 1–8 to determine whether each statement is true or false.

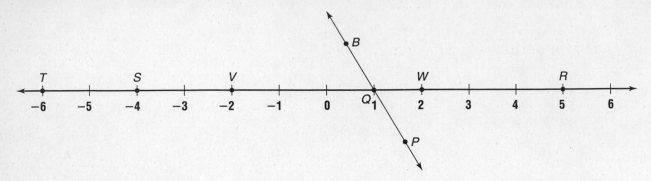

1. $\overline{PB}$ bisects $\overline{RS}$. **false**

2. S is the midpoint of $\overline{TV}$. **true**

3. $\overline{SV} \cong \overline{TS}$ **true**

4. V is the midpoint of $\overline{TW}$. **true**

5. W bisects $\overline{VR}$. **false**

6. $\overline{WR} \cong \overline{QV}$ **true**

7. $\overline{SW}$ is longer than $\overline{VR}$. **false**

8. $VW \leq TV$ **true**

Given the coordinate of one endpoint of $\overline{AB}$ and its midpoint M, find the coordinates of the other endpoint.

9. $A(0, 9)$, $M(2, 5)$ **B (4, 1)**

10. $B(-5, 1)$, $M(1, -1)$ **A (7, −3)**

11. $A(-2, 3)$ $M(0.5, 0.5)$ **B (3, −2)**

12. $A(4, 2)$, $M(-2, 10)$ **B (−8, 18)**

In the figure at the right, $\overline{WY}$ bisects $\overline{UV}$ at Y and $\overline{UY}$ bisects TW at X. For each situation, find the value of x and the measure of the indicated segment.

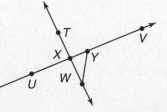

13. $UY = 4x - 3$, $YV = x$; UV **1, 2**

14. $UV = x + 6$, $UY = x - 1$; YV **8, 7**

15. $TX = 2x + 1$, $XW = x + 7$; TW **6, 26**

16. $WX = x + 5$, $TW = 4x + 5$: TX **2.5, 7.5**

NAME_____ DATE _____

Practice

Exploring Angles

Refer to the figure at the right to answer each question.

1. Give another name for $\angle 1$.

2. Name the vertex of $\angle EBD$.

3. Does $\angle ABE$ appear to be acute, obtuse, right, or straight?

4. If $m\angle DBF = 35$, what is the measure of $\angle EBF$?

5. Name a pair of opposite rays.

6. Name a point in the interior of $\angle EBF$.

7. Name three angles with $\overrightarrow{BE}$ as a side?

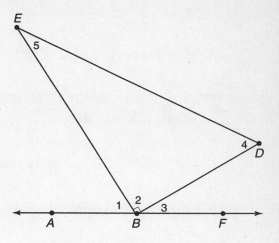

In the figure, $\overrightarrow{XP}$ and $\overrightarrow{XT}$ are opposite rays and $\overrightarrow{XQ}$ bisects $\angle PXS$. For each situation, find the value of x and the measure of the indicated angle.

8. $m\angle SXT = 4x + 1$, $m\angle QXS = 2x - 2$, $m\angle QXT = 125$; $m\angle QXS$

9. $m\angle PXR = 3x$, $m\angle RXT = 5x + 20$, $m\angle RXT$

10. $m\angle RXQ = x + 15$, $m\angle RXS = 5x - 7$, $m\angle QXS = 3x + 5$; $m\angle RXS$

11. $m\angle RXQ = 2x + 7$, $m\angle RXP = 3x - 11$, $m\angle PXS = x + 37$; $m\angle QXS$

12. $m\angle TXS = x + 3$, $m\angle SXR = 2x + 9$, $m\angle RXP = 4x - 7$; $m\angle PXS$

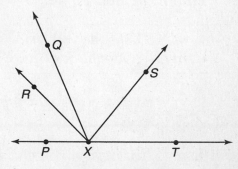

NAME_____ DATE _____

Practice

Exploring Angles

Refer to the figure at the right to answer each question.

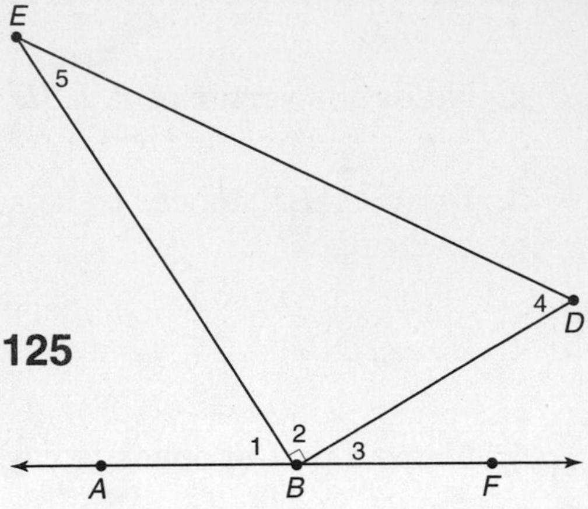

1. Give another name for ∠1. **∠ ABE or ∠ EBA**

2. Name the vertex of ∠EBD. **B**

3. Does ∠ABE appear to be acute, obtuse, right, or straight? **acute**

4. If $m\angle DBF = 35$, what is the measure of ∠EBF? **125**

5. Name a pair of opposite rays. $\overrightarrow{BA}$ **and** $\overrightarrow{BF}$

6. Name a point in the interior of ∠EBF. **D**

7. Name three angles with $\overrightarrow{BE}$ as a side? **∠ FBE, ∠ DBE, ∠ ABE**

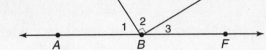

In the figure, $\overrightarrow{XP}$ and $\overrightarrow{XT}$ are opposite rays and $\overrightarrow{XQ}$ bisects ∠ PXS. For each situation, find the value of x and the measure of the indicated angle.

8. $m\angle SXT = 4x + 1$, $m\angle QXS = 2x - 2$, $m\angle QXT = 125$; $m\angle QXS$ **21, 40**

9. $m\angle PXR = 3x$, $m\angle RXT = 5x + 20$, $m\angle RXT$ **20, 120**

10. $m\angle RXQ = x + 15$, $m\angle RXS = 5x - 7$, $m\angle QXS = 3x + 5$; $m\angle RXS$ **27, 128**

11. $m\angle RXQ = 2x + 7$, $m\angle RXP = 3x - 11$, $m\angle PXS = x + 37$; $m\angle QXS$ **5, 21**

12. $m\angle TXS = x + 3$, $m\angle SXR = 2x + 9$, $m\angle RXP = 4x - 7$; $m\angle PXS$ **25, 152**

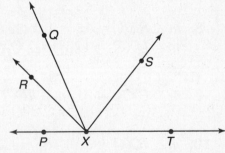

T6   *Geometry*

NAME________________________ DATE __________

Practice

Student Edition
Pages 53–60

Angle Relationships

Refer to the figure at the right to answer each question.

A
F
B
E
D
C

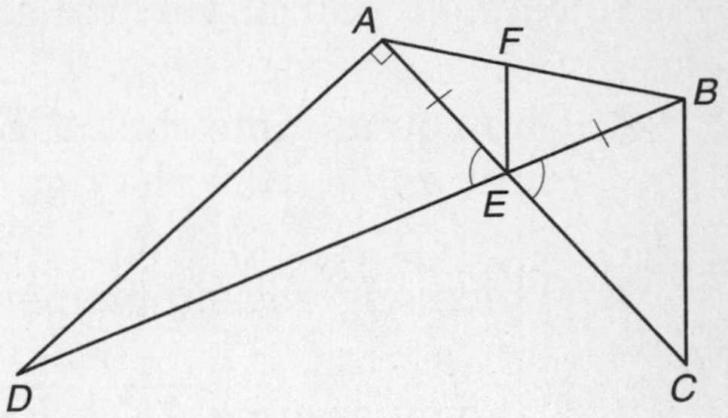

1. Name a pair of vertical angles.
2. Can you assume that $\angle EFB$ is a right angle from the figure?
3. Which angle is supplementary to $\angle FEB$?
4. Can you assume $\overline{AE} \cong \overline{BE}$?
5. Can you assume that F bisects $\overline{AB}$ from the figure?
6. Name an angle adjacent, but not supplementary, to $\angle DEA$.

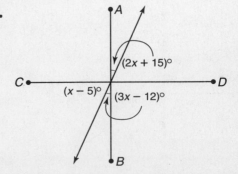

Find the value of x and m∠ABC.

7.

A
B
(4x + 50)°
(2x + 60)°
C

8.

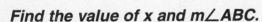

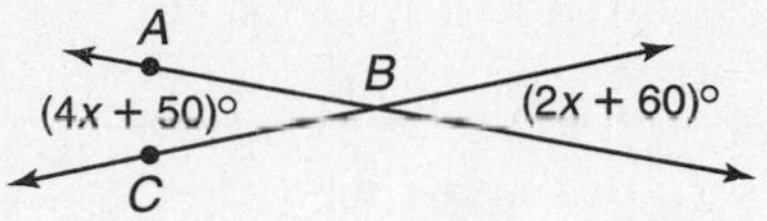

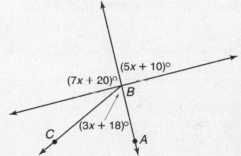

(5x + 10)°
(7x + 20)°
B
(3x + 18)°
C
A

For each figure, find the value of x. Then determine if $\overline{AB} \perp \overline{CD}$.

9.

C
(6x – 3)°
(7x – 11)°
A
(5x + 5)°
B
D

10.

A
(2x + 15)°
C
D
(x – 5)°
(3x – 12)°
B

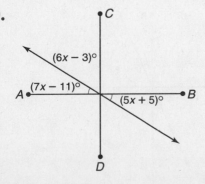

Practice

Angle Relationships

Refer to the figure at the right to answer each question.

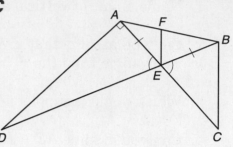

1. Name a pair of vertical angles. **∠ AED and ∠ BEC**

2. Can you assume that ∠EFB is a right angle from the figure? **no**

3. Which angle is supplementary to ∠FEB? **∠ FED**

4. Can you assume $\overline{AE} \cong \overline{BE}$? **yes**

5. Can you assume that F bisects $\overline{AB}$ from the figure? **no**

6. Name an angle adjacent, but not supplementary, to ∠DEA. **∠ AEF**

Find the value of x and m∠ABC.

7.

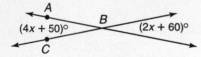

(4x + 50)°
B
(2x + 60)°
C

5, 70

8.

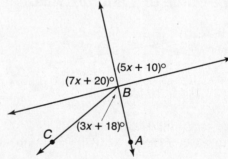

(5x + 10)°
(7x + 20)°
B
(3x + 18)°
C
A

12.5, 55.5

For each figure, find the value of x. Then determine if $\overline{AB} \perp \overline{CD}$.

9.

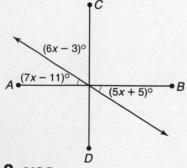

C
(6x − 3)°
(7x − 11)°
A
(5x + 5)°
B
D

8, yes

10.

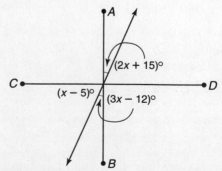

A
(2x + 15)°
C
(x − 5)°
(3x − 12)°
D
B

27, no

Geometry

NAME_____ DATE _____

Practice

Inductive Reasoning and Conjecturing

Determine if the conjecture is <u>true</u> or <u>false</u> based on the given information. Explain your answer and give a counterexample for any false conjecture.

1. Given: noncollinear points A, B, C, and D
Conjecture: A, B, C, and D are coplanar.

2. Given: A, B, C, and D are collinear points.
Conjecture: $AB + BC + CD = AD$

3. Given: $\angle A$ and $\angle B$ are right angles.
Conjecture: $\angle A \cong \angle B$

4. Given: Point C between H and V.
Conjecture: $\angle HCV$ is a straight angle.

Write a conjecture based on the given information. If appropriate, draw a figure to illustrate your conjecture.

5. $\overline{AB}$, $\overline{CD}$, and $\overline{EF}$ intersect at X.

6. $\angle MNO$ and $\angle PNO$ are adjacent angles.

7. A (3, 1), B (3, -5), C (3, 7).

8. A, B, C, and D are coplanar points.

NAME_____ DATE _____

Practice

Inductive Reasoning and Conjecturing

Determine if the conjecture is _true_ or _false_ based on the given information. Explain your answer and give a counterexample for any false conjecture.

1. Given: noncollinear points A, B, C, and D
   Conjecture: A, B, C, and D are coplanar. **false;**

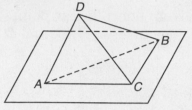

2. Given: A, B, C, and D are collinear points.
   Conjecture: $AB + BC + CD = AD$
   false; **$AB + BC + CD > AD$**

3. Given: $\angle A$ and $\angle B$ are right angles.
   Conjecture: $\angle A \cong \angle B$ **true; $m\angle A = 90$, $m\angle B = 90$**

4. Given: Point C between H and V.
   Conjecture: $\angle HCV$ is a straight angle. **True;**
   $\overrightarrow{CH}$ and $\overrightarrow{CV}$ are opposite rays.

Answers for Exercises 5–8 may vary. Sample answers are given.
Write a conjecture based on the given information. If appropriate, draw a figure to illustrate your conjecture.

5. $\overline{AB}$, $\overline{CD}$, and $\overline{EF}$ intersect at X. **A, B, C, D, E, F, and X are noncollinear. (true)**

6. $\angle MNO$ and $\angle PNO$ are adjacent angles. **Point O is not between M and P. (true)**

7. A (3, 1), B (3, –5), C (3, 7). **Points A, B, and C lie on the same vertical line. (true)**

8. A, B, C, and D are coplanar points. $\angle ABC$ and $\angle ABD$ are **adjacent angles. (false)**

If-Then Statements and Postulates

Identify the hypothesis and conclusion of each conditional statement.

1. If $3x - 1 = 7$, then $x = 2$.

2. If Carl scores 85%, then he passes.

Write each conditional statement in if-then form.

3. All students like vacations.

4. The game will be played provided it doesn't rain.

Write the converse of each conditional. Determine if the converse is _true_ or _false_. It if is false, give a counterexample.

5. If it rains, then it is cloudy.

6. If x is an even number, then x is divisible by 2.

In the figure, P, Q, R, and S are in plane $\mathcal{N}$. Use the postulates you have learned to determine whether each statement is _true_ or _false_.

7. R, S, and T are collinear.

8. There is only one plane that contains all the points R, S, and Q.

9. $\angle PQT$ lies in plane $\mathcal{N}$.

10. $\angle SPR$ lies in plane $\mathcal{N}$.

11. If X and Y are two points on line m, then $\overleftrightarrow{XY}$ intersects plane $\mathcal{N}$ at P.

12. Point K is on plane $\mathcal{N}$.

13. $\mathcal{N}$ contains $\overline{RS}$.

14. T lies in plane $\mathcal{N}$.

15. R, P, S, and T are coplanar.

16. ℓ and m intersect.

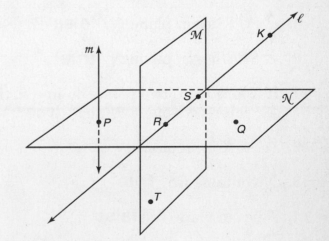

NAME_____ DATE _____

Practice

If-Then Statements and Postulates

Identify the hypothesis and conclusion of each conditional statement.

1. If $3x - 1 = 7$, then $x = 2$.
   **Hypothesis: $3x - 1 = 7$
   Conclusion: $x = 2$**

2. If Carl scores 85%, then he passes.
   **Hypothesis: Carl scores 85%
   Conclusion: he passes**

Write each conditional statement in if-then form.

3. All students like vacations. **If a person is a student, then that person likes vacations.**

4. The game will be played provided it doesn't rain. **If it doesn't rain, then the game will be played.**

Write the converse of each conditional. Determine if the converse is _true_ or _false_. It if is false, give a counterexample.

5. If it rains, then it is cloudy. **If it is cloudy, then it rains; false. It can be cloudy without raining.**

6. If x is an even number, then x is divisible by 2. **If x is divisible by 2, then x is an even number; true.**

In the figure, P, Q, R, and S are in plane $\mathcal{N}$. Use the postulates you have learned to determine whether each statement is _true_ or _false_.

7. R, S, and T are collinear. **false**

8. There is only one plane that contains all the points R, S, and Q. **true**

9. $\angle PQT$ lies in plane $\mathcal{N}$. **false**

10. $\angle SPR$ lies in plane $\mathcal{N}$. **true**

11. If X and Y are two points on line m, then $\overleftrightarrow{XY}$ intersects plane $\mathcal{N}$ at P. **true**

12. Point K is on plane $\mathcal{N}$. **true**

13. $\mathcal{N}$ contains $\overline{RS}$. **true**

14. T lies in plane $\mathcal{N}$. **false**

15. R, P, S, and T are coplanar. **false**

16. ℓ and m intersect. **false**

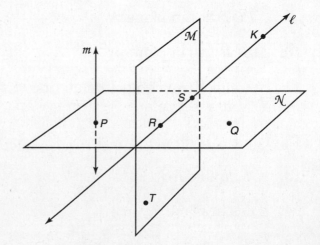

NAME_____ DATE _____

Practice

Deductive Reasoning

Determine if a valid conclusion can be reached from the two true statements using the Law of Detachment or the Law of Syllogism. If a valid conclusion is possible, state it and the law that is used. If a valid conclusion does not follow, write no conclusion.

1. If Jim is a Texan, then he is an American.
   Jim is a Texan.

2. If Spot is a dog, then he has four legs.
   Spot has four legs.

3. If Rachel lives in Tampa, then Rachel lives in Florida.
   If Rachel lives in Florida, then Rachel lives in the United States.

4. If October 12 is a Monday, then October 13 is a Tuesday.
   October 12 is a Monday.

5. If Henry studies his algebra, then he passes the test.
   If Henry passes the test, then he will get a good grade.

Determine if statement (3) follows from statements (1) and (2) by the Law of Detachment or the Law of Syllogism. If it does, state which law was used. If it does not, write invalid.

6. (1) If the measure of an angle is greater than 90, then it is obtuse.
   (2) $m \angle T$ is greater than 90.
   (3) $\angle T$ is obtuse.

7. (1) If Pedro is taking history, then he will study about World War II.
   (2) Pedro will study about World War II.
   (3) Pedro is taking history.

8. (1) If Julie works after school, then she works in a department store.
   (2) Julie works after school.
   (3) Julie works in a department store.

9. (1) If William is reading, then he is reading a magazine.
   (2) If William is reading a magazine, then he is reading a magazine about computers.
   (3) If William is reading, then he is reading a magazine about computers.

10. **Look for a Pattern** Tanya likes to burn candles. She has found that, once a candle has burned, she can melt 3 candle stubs, add a new wick, and have one more candle to burn. How many total candles can she burn from a box of 15 candles?

NAME_____ DATE _____

Practice

Deductive Reasoning

Determine if a valid conclusion can be reached from the two true statements using the Law of Detachment or the Law of Syllogism. If a valid conclusion is possible, state it and the law that is used. If a valid conclusion does not follow, write no conclusion.

1. If Jim is a Texan, then he is an American.
   Jim is a Texan. **Jim is an American; detachment.**

2. If Spot is a dog, then he has four legs.
   Spot has four legs. **no conclusion**

3. If Rachel lives in Tampa, then Rachel lives in Florida.
   If Rachel lives in Florida, then Rachel lives in the United States.
   If Rachel lives in Tampa, then Rachel lives in the United States; syllogism.

4. If October 12 is a Monday, then October 13 is a Tuesday.
   October 12 is a Monday. **October 13 is a Tuesday; detachment.**

5. If Henry studies his algebra, then he passes the test.
   If Henry passes the test, then he will get a good grade. **If Henry studies his algebra, then he will get a good grade; syllogism.**

Determine if statement (3) follows from statements (1) and (2) by the Law of Detachment or the Law of Syllogism. If it does, state which law was used. If it does not, write invalid.

6. (1) If the measure of an angle is greater than 90, then it is obtuse.
   (2) $m \angle T$ is greater than 90.
   (3) $\angle T$ is obtuse. **yes; detachment**

7. (1) If Pedro is taking history, then he will study about World War II.
   (2) Pedro will study about World War II.
   (3) Pedro is taking history. **invalid**

8. (1) If Julie works after school, then she works in a department store.
   (2) Julie works after school.
   (3) Julie works in a department store. **yes; detachment**

9. (1) If William is reading, then he is reading a magazine.
   (2) If William is reading a magazine, then he is reading a magazine about computers.
   (3) If William is reading, then he is reading a magazine about computers. **yes; syllogism**

10. **Look for a Pattern**   Tanya likes to burn candles. She has found that, once a candle has burned, she can melt 3 candle stubs, add a new wick, and have one more candle to burn. How many total candles can she burn from a box of 15 candles? **22**

Geometry

NAME_____ DATE _____

Practice

Integration: Algebra
Using Proof in Algebra

Name the property of equality that justifies each statement.

1. If $m\angle A = m\angle B$, then $m\angle B = m\angle A$.

2. If $x + 3 = 17$, then $x = 14$.

3. $xy = xy$

4. If $7x = 42$, then $x = 6$.

5. If $XY - YZ = XM$, then $XM + YZ = XY$.

6. $2(x + 4) = 2x + 8$.

7. If $m\angle A + m\angle B = 90$, and $m\angle A = 30$, then $30 + m\angle B = 90$.

8. If $x = y + 3$ and $y + 3 = 10$, then $x = 10$.

Complete each proof by naming the property that justifies each statement.

9. Prove that if $2(x - 3) = 8$, then $x = 7$.
   Given: $2(x - 3) = 8$
   Prove: $x = 7$
   Proof:

Statements	Reasons
a. $2(x - 3) = 8$	a. _____
b. $2x - 6 = 8$	b. _____
c. $2x = 14$	c. _____
d. $x = 7$	d. _____

10. Prove that if $3x - 4 = \frac{1}{2}x + 6$, then $x = 4$.
    Given: $3x - 4 = \frac{1}{2}x + 6$
    Prove: $x = 4$
    Proof:

Statements	Reasons
a. $3x - 4 = \frac{1}{2}x + 6$	a. _____
b. $\frac{5}{2}x - 4 = 6$	b. _____
c. $\frac{5}{2}x = 10$	c. _____
d. $x = 4$	d. _____

Geometry

Practice

Integration: Algebra
Using Proof in Algebra

Name the property of equality that justifies each statement.

1. If $m\angle A = m\angle B$, then $m\angle B = m\angle A$. **symmetric**

2. If $x + 3 = 17$, then $x = 14$. **subtraction**

3. $xy = xy$ **reflexive**

4. If $7x = 42$, then $x = 6$. **division**

5. If $XY - YZ = XM$, then $XM + YZ = XY$. **addition**

6. $2(x + 4) = 2x + 8$. **distributive**

7. If $m\angle A + m\angle B = 90$, and $m\angle A = 30$, then $30 + m\angle B = 90$. **substitution**

8. If $x = y + 3$ and $y + 3 = 10$, then $x = 10$. **transitive**

Complete each proof by naming the property that justifies each statement.

9. Prove that if $2(x - 3) = 8$, then $x = 7$.
   Given: $2(x - 3) = 8$
   Prove: $x = 7$
   Proof:

Statements	Reasons
a. $2(x - 3) = 8$	a. Given
b. $2x - 6 = 8$	b. Distributive Property
c. $2x = 14$	c. Addition Property (=)
d. $x = 7$	d. Division Property (=)

10. Prove that if $3x - 4 = \frac{1}{2}x + 6$, then $x = 4$.
    Given: $3x - 4 = \frac{1}{2}x + 6$
    Prove: $x = 4$
    Proof:

Statements	Reasons
a. $3x - 4 = \frac{1}{2}x + 6$	a. Given
b. $\frac{5}{2}x - 4 = 6$	b. Subtraction Property (=)
c. $\frac{5}{2}x = 10$	c. Addition Property (=)
d. $x = 4$	d. Multiplication Property (=)

Verifying Segment Relationships

Complete each proof.

1. Given: $AD = 2AB + BC$
Prove: $\overline{AB} \cong \overline{CD}$
Proof:

Statements	Reasons
a. $AD = 2AB + BC$	**a.** _____
b. $AD = AB + BC + CD$	**b.** _____
c. $2AB + BC = AB + BC + CD$	**c.** _____
d. $AB = CD$	**d.** _____
e. $\overline{AB} \cong \overline{CD}$	**e.** _____

2. Given: B is between A and D.
    C is between A and D.
Prove: $AB + BD = AC + CD$
Proof:

Statements	Reasons
a. B is between A and D. C is between A and D.	**a.** _____
b. $AB + BD = AD$	**b.** _____
c. $AC + CD = AD$	**c.** _____
d. $AD = AC + CD$	**d.** _____
e. $AB + BD = AC + CD$	**e.** _____

Write a two-column proof.

3. Given: B is the midpoint of $\overline{AC}$.
Prove: $AB + CD = BD$
Proof:

Statements	Reasons

Verifying Segment Relationships

Complete each proof.

1. **Given:** $AD = 2AB + BC$
   Prove: $\overline{AB} \cong \overline{CD}$
   Proof:

Statements	Reasons
a. $AD = 2AB + BC$	a. **Given**
b. $AD = AB + BC + CD$	b. **Segment Addition Postulate**
c. $2AB + BC = AB + BC + CD$	c. **Substitution Property (=)**
d. $AB = CD$	d. **Subtraction Property (=)**
e. $\overline{AB} \cong \overline{CD}$	e. **Definition of congruent segments**

2. **Given:** B is between A and D.
   C is between A and D.
   Prove: $AB + BD = AC + CD$
   Proof:

Statements	Reasons
a. B is between A and D. C is between A and D.	a. **Given**
b. $AB + BD = AD$	b. **Segment Addition Postulate**
c. $AC + CD = AD$	c. **Segment Addition Postulate**
d. $AD = AC + CD$	d. **Symmetric Property (=)**
e. $AB + BD = AC + CD$	e. **Transitive Property (=)**

Write a two-column proof.

3. **Given:** B is the midpoint of $\overline{AC}$.
   Prove: $AB + CD = BD$
   Proof:

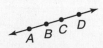

Statements	Reasons
a. B is the midpoint of $\overline{AC}$.	a. Given
b. $AB = BC$	b. Definition of midpoint
c. $BC + CD = BD$	c. Segment Addition Postulate
d. $AB + CD = BD$	d. Substitution Property (=)

Geometry

Practice

Verifying Angle Relationships

Complete each statement if m∠BGC = 43 and m∠DGE = 56.

1. ∠FGA ≅ _?_

2. ∠BGF and _?_ are supplementary.

3. m∠CGD = _?_

4. m∠AGF = _?_

5. ∠EGC and _?_ are supplementary.

6. m∠AGB = _?_

7. m∠AGC = _?_

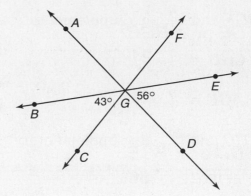

Write a two-column proof.

8. **Given:** ∠AEC ≅ ∠DEB
   Prove: ∠AEB ≅ ∠DEC
   Proof:

Statements	Reasons

NAME ______________________ DATE ____________

Practice

Student Edition
Pages 107–114

Verifying Angle Relationships

Complete each statement if m∠BGC = 43 and m∠DGE = 56.

1. ∠FGA ≅ _?_ **∠DGC**

2. ∠BGF and _?_ are supplementary. **∠FGE or ∠BGC**

3. m∠CGD = _?_ **81**

4. m∠AGF = _?_ **81**

5. ∠EGC and _?_ are supplementary. **∠BGC or ∠FGE**

6. m∠AGB = _?_ **56**

7. m∠AGC = _?_ **99**

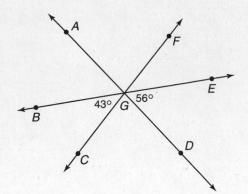

Write a two-column proof.

8. Given: ∠AEC ≅ ∠DEB
Prove: ∠AEB ≅ ∠DEC
Proof:

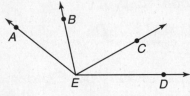

Statements	Reasons
a. ∠AEC ≅ ∠DEB	**a. Given**
b. m∠AEC = m∠DEB	**b. Definition of congruent angles**
c. m∠AEC = m∠AEB + m∠BEC, m∠DEB = m∠DEC + m∠BEC	**c. Angle Addition Postulate**
d. m∠AEB + m∠BEC = m∠DEC + m∠BEC	**d. Transitive Property (=)**
e. m∠AEB = m∠DEC	**e. Subtraction Property (=)**
f. ∠AEB ≅ ∠DEC	**f. Definition of congruent angles**

NAME______________________________ DATE ____________

Practice

Student Edition
Pages 124–129

Parallel Lines and Transversals

State the transversal that forms each pair of angles. Then identify the special name for the angle pair.

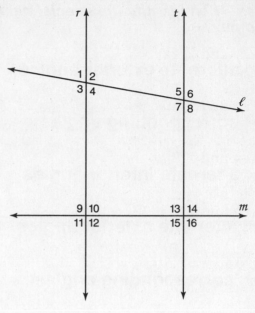

1. $\angle 1$ and $\angle 12$

2. $\angle 2$ and $\angle 10$

3. $\angle 4$ and $\angle 9$

4. $\angle 6$ and $\angle 3$

5. $\angle 14$ and $\angle 10$

6. $\angle 7$ and $\angle 13$

The three-dimensional figure shown at the right is called a right pentagonal prism.

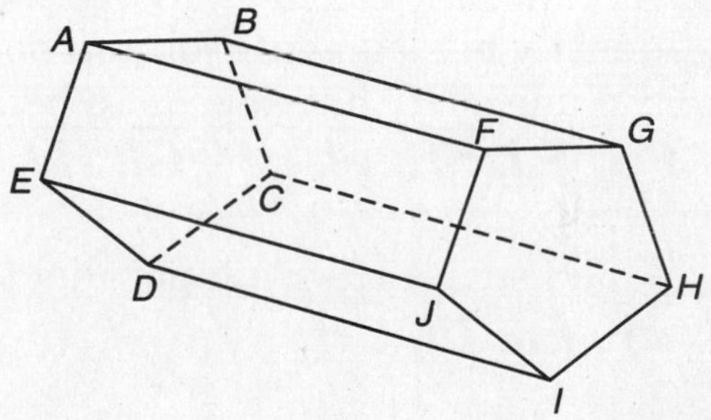

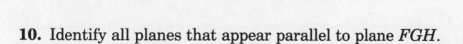

7. Identify all segments joining points marked in plane *JIH* that appear to be skew to $\overline{EB}$.

8. Which segments seem parallel to $\overline{BG}$?

9. Which segments seem parallel to $\overline{GH}$?

10. Identify all planes that appear parallel to plane *FGH*.

11. Draw a Diagram At a town's bicentennial celebration, men dressed up as settlers and tipped their hats whenever they met another man. At a town meeting, ten men were present. How many times were pairs of hats tipped as two men met for the first time?

3–1

Practice

Parallel Lines and Transversals

State the transversal that forms each pair of angles. Then identify the special name for the angle pair.

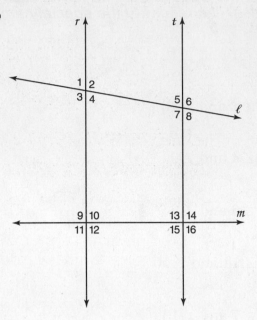

1. ∠1 and ∠12
   r; alternate exterior angles

2. ∠2 and ∠10
   r; corresponding angles

3. ∠4 and ∠9
   r; alternate interior angles

4. ∠6 and ∠3
   ℓ; alternate exterior angles

5. ∠14 and ∠10
   m; corresponding angles

6. ∠7 and ∠13
   t; consecutive interior angles

The three-dimensional figure shown at the right is called a right pentagonal prism.

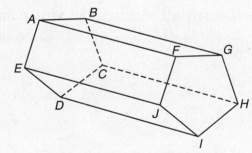

7. Identify all segments joining points marked in plane *JIH* that appear to be skew to $\overline{EB}$.
   FG, FJ, FH, FI, GH, GI, HJ, IJ

8. Which segments seem parallel to $\overline{BG}$?
   AF, EJ, DI, CH

9. Which segments seem parallel to $\overline{GH}$? **BC**

10. Identify all planes that appear parallel to plane *FGH*. **plane ABC**

11. **Draw a Diagram** At a town's bicentennial celebration, men dressed up as settlers and tipped their hats whenever they met another man. At a town meeting, ten men were present. How many times were pairs of hats tipped as two men met for the first time? **45**

     Geometry

3–2

NAME______________________________ DATE ______________

Practice

Student Edition
Pages 131–137

Angles and Parallel Lines

In the figure, $\ell \parallel m$. Find the measure of each angle.

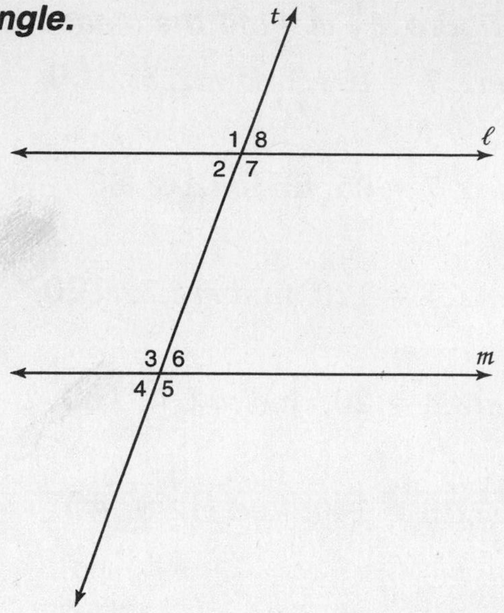

1. If $m\angle 7 = 100$, find $m\angle 3$.

2. If $m\angle 7 = 95$, find $m\angle 6$.

3. If $m\angle 1 = 120$, find $m\angle 5$.

4. If $m\angle 4 = 20$, find $m\angle 7$.

5. If $m\angle 3 = 140$, find $m\angle 8$.

6. If $m\angle 4 = 30$, find $m\angle 1$.

7. If $m\angle 4 = 40$, find $m\angle 2$.

8. If $m\angle 7 = 125$, find $m\angle 4$.

9. If $\ell \perp t$, find $m\angle 3$.

10. If $m\angle 1 + m\angle 3 = 230$, find $m\angle 6$.

In the figure, $s \parallel t$. Find the measure of each angle.

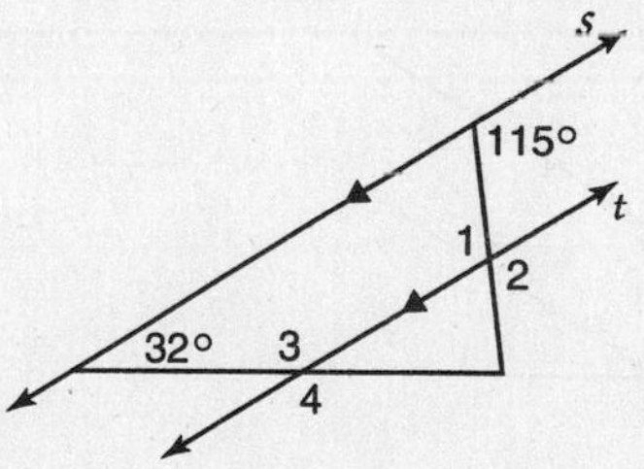

11. $m\angle 1$

12. $m\angle 2$

13. $m\angle 3$

14. $m\angle 4$

15. In the figure, $r \parallel s$. Find the value of x.

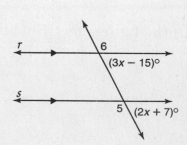

NAME_____ DATE _____

Practice

Angles and Parallel Lines

In the figure, $\ell \parallel m$. Find the measure of each angle.

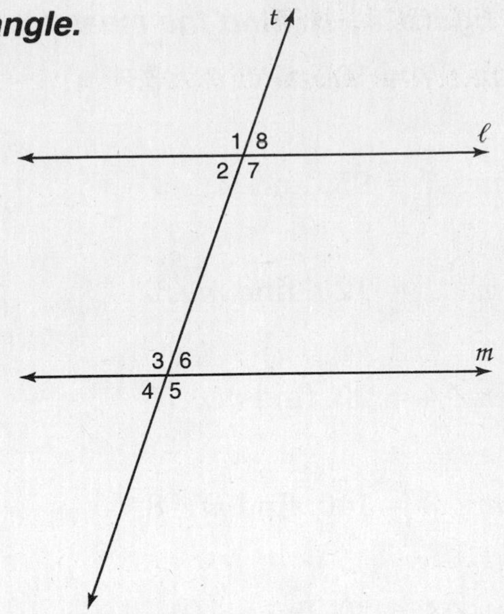

1. If $m\angle 7 = 100$, find $m\angle 3$. **100**

2. If $m\angle 7 = 95$, find $m\angle 6$. **85**

3. If $m\angle 1 = 120$, find $m\angle 5$. **120**

4. If $m\angle 4 = 20$, find $m\angle 7$. **160**

5. If $m\angle 3 = 140$, find $m\angle 8$. **40**

6. If $m\angle 4 = 30$, find $m\angle 1$. **150**

7. If $m\angle 4 = 40$, find $m\angle 2$. **40**

8. If $m\angle 7 = 125$, find $m\angle 4$. **55**

9. If $\ell \perp t$, find $m\angle 3$. **90**

10. If $m\angle 1 + m\angle 3 = 230$, find $m\angle 6$. **65**

In the figure, $s \parallel t$. Find the measure of each angle.

11. $m\angle 1$ **115**

12. $m\angle 2$ **115**

13. $m\angle 3$ **148**

14. $m\angle 4$ **148**

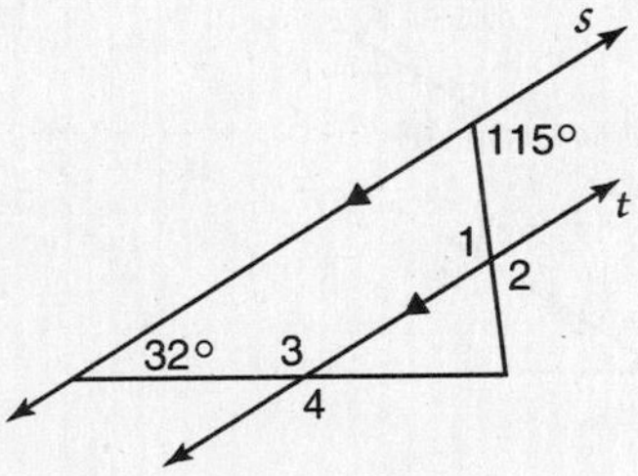

15. In the figure, $r \parallel s$. Find the value of x. **22**

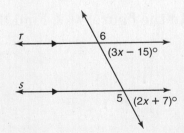

Geometry

NAME_____ DATE _____

Practice

Integration: Algebra
Slopes of Lines

Determine the slope of each line named below.

1. a

2. b

3. c

4. d

5. any line parallel to b

6. any line perpendicular to d

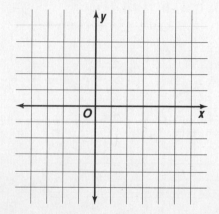

Graph the line that satisfies each description.

7. slope = -3, passes through $P(1, -2)$

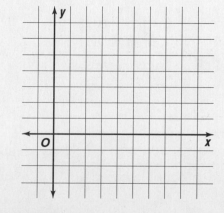

8. passes through $P(-1, 2)$ and is perpendicular to the line determined by $A(1, 4)$ and $B(2, 7)$

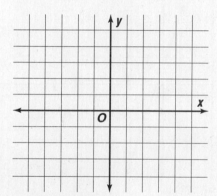

Determine the value of r so that a line through the points with the given coordinates has the given slope. Draw a sketch of each situation.

9. $(5, 3)$, $(r, 6)$; slope = 1

10. $(2, r)$, $(-2, 6)$; slope = $\frac{1}{2}$

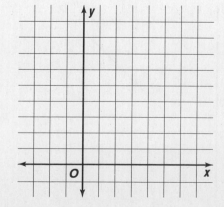

Geometry

Integration: Algebra
Slopes of Lines

Determine the slope of each line named below.

1. a $\dfrac{2}{3}$

2. b **3**

3. c **undefined**

4. d **-2**

5. any line parallel to b **3**

6. any line perpendicular to d $\dfrac{1}{2}$

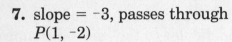

Graph the line that satisfies each description.

7. slope = -3, passes through
   $P(1, -2)$

8. passes through $P(-1, 2)$ and is
   perpendicular to the line determined
   by $A(1, 4)$ and $B(2, 7)$

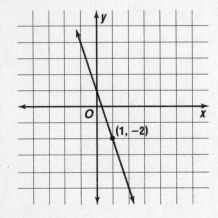

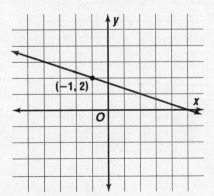

**Determine the value of r so that a line through the points with
the given coordinates has the given slope. Draw a sketch of
each situation.**

9. $(5, 3)$, $(r, 6)$; slope = 1 **8**

10. $(2, r)$, $(-2, 6)$; slope = $\dfrac{1}{2}$ **8**

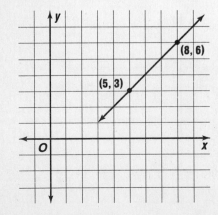

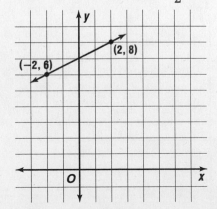

NAME_____ DATE _____

Practice

Proving Lines Parallel

For Exercises 1–6, find the value of x so that $\ell \parallel m$.

1.

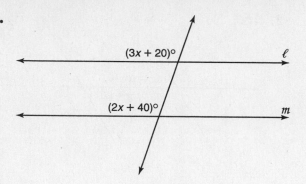

$(3x + 20)°$ ℓ

$(2x + 40)°$ m

2.

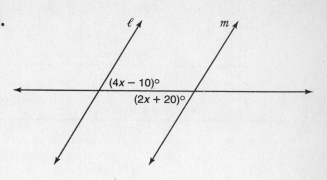

ℓ m

$(4x - 10)°$

$(2x + 20)°$

3.

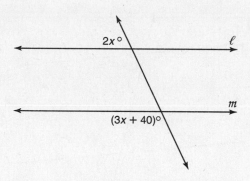

$2x°$ ℓ

m

$(3x + 40)°$

4.

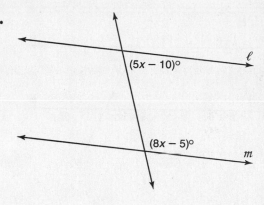

$(5x - 10)°$ ℓ

$(8x - 5)°$ m

5.

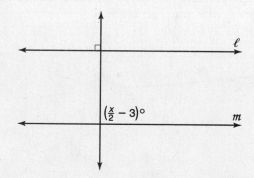

ℓ

$\left(\frac{x}{2} - 3\right)°$ m

6.

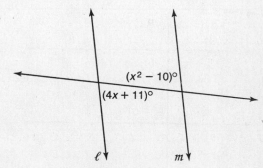

$(x^2 - 10)°$

$(4x + 11)°$

ℓ m

7. If $\ell \not\parallel m$, can $x = 50$? Justify your answer.

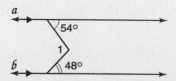

$(3x + 5)°$ ℓ

$(x - 5)°$ m

8. Find $m\angle 1$ for the figure at the right.

a

$54°$

1

b $48°$

17

3-4

Practice

Proving Lines Parallel

For Exercises 1–6, find the value of x so that $\ell \parallel m$.

1. **20**

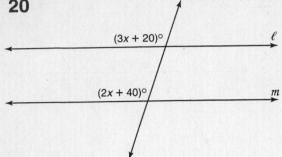

$(3x + 20)°$ ℓ

$(2x + 40)°$ m

2. **15**

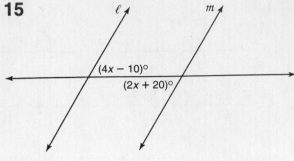

$(4x - 10)°$
$(2x + 20)°$

3. **28**

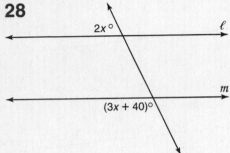

$2x°$ ℓ

m

$(3x + 40)°$

4. **15**

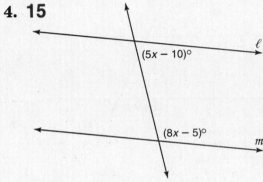

$(5x - 10)°$ ℓ

$(8x - 5)°$ m

5. **186**

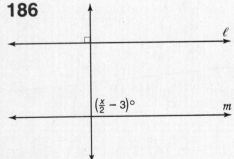

ℓ

$\left(\frac{x}{2} - 3\right)°$ m

6. **7**

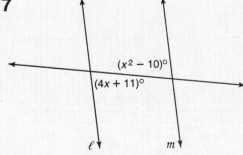

$(x^2 - 10)°$
$(4x + 11)°$

ℓ m

$(3x + 5)°$ ℓ

$(x - 5)°$ m

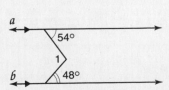

7. If $\ell \not\parallel m$, can $x = 50$? Justify your answer.
   Yes; the lines are parallel only if x = 45.

8. Find $m\angle 1$ for the figure at the right. **102**

a

$54°$

1

b $48°$

Practice

Parallels and Distance

Draw the segment that represents the distance indicated.

1. P to $\overleftrightarrow{RS}$

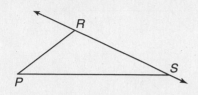

2. B to $\overline{AD}$

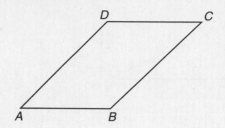

Graph each equation and plot the given ordered pair. Then construct a perpendicular segment and find the distance from the point to the line.

3. $y = x + 2$, $(2, -2)$

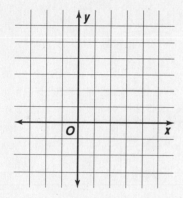

4. $x + y = 2$, $(3, 3)$

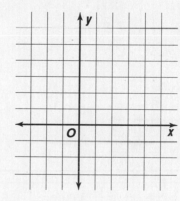

In the figure below, $\overline{BH} \perp \overline{AE}$, $\overline{CF} \perp \overline{AE}$, $\overline{BH} \perp \overline{BC}$, $\overline{BC} \perp \overline{CF}$, and $\overline{GD} \perp \overline{CE}$. Name the segment whose length represents the distance between the following points and lines.

5. B to $\overline{AE}$

6. G to $\overline{CE}$

7. C to $\overline{BH}$

8. F to $\overline{BC}$

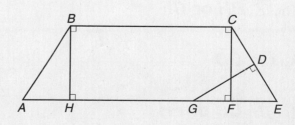

Practice

Parallels and Distance

Draw the segment that represents the distance indicated.

1. P to $\overrightarrow{RS}$

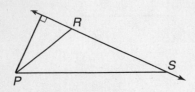

2. B to $\overline{AD}$

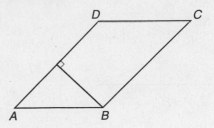

Graph each equation and plot the given ordered pair. Then construct a perpendicular segment and find the distance from the point to the line.

3. $y = x + 2$, $(2, -2)$ **$3\sqrt{2}$**

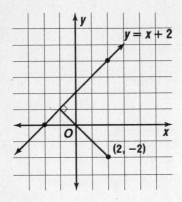

4. $x + y = 2$, $(3, 3)$ **$2\sqrt{2}$**

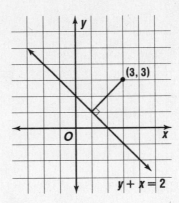

In the figure below, $\overline{BH} \perp \overline{AE}$, $\overline{CF} \perp \overline{AE}$, $\overline{BH} \perp \overline{BC}$, $\overline{BC} \perp \overline{CF}$, and $\overline{GD} \perp \overline{CE}$. Name the segment whose length represents the distance between the following points and lines.

5. B to $\overline{AE}$ **$\overline{BH}$ or $\overline{CF}$**

6. G to $\overline{CE}$ **$\overline{GD}$**

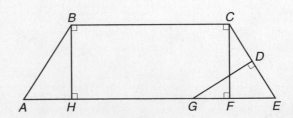

7. C to $\overline{BH}$ **$\overline{CB}$ or $\overline{FH}$**

8. F to $\overline{BC}$ **$\overline{FC}$ or $\overline{BH}$**

NAME_____ DATE _____

Practice

Student Edition
Pages 163–169

Integration: Non-Euclidean Geometry
Spherical Geometry

*Use a globe or world map to name the latitude and longitude
of each city.*

1. Bogota, Colombia

2. Cairo, Egypt

3. Melbourne, Australia

4. Fairbanks, Alaska

5. Nairobi, Kenya

6. London, England

7. Cape Town, South Africa

8. Julianehab, Greenland

9. La Paz, Bolivia

*Use a globe or world map to name the city located near each
set of coordinates.*

10. 34°S, 59°W

11. 30°N, 90°W

12. 48°N, 123°W

13. 7°S, 107°E

14. 9°N, 38°E

15. 51°N, 14°E

16. 23°S, 46°W

17. 18°N, 99°W

18. 35°S, 173°E

*For each property listed from plane Euclidean geometry, write
a corresponding statement for non-Euclidean spherical
geometry.*

19. Two lines intersecting to form four right angles are
perpendicular.

20. Through any two points in a plane there is a unique and
infinite straight line.

21. An infinite number of lines can be drawn through a point in
a plane.

Geometry

Practice

Integration: Non-Euclidean Geometry
Spherical Geometry

Use a globe or world map to name the latitude and longitude of each city.

1. Bogota, Colombia
5°N, 75°W

2. Cairo, Egypt
30°N, 32°E

3. Melbourne, Australia
37°S, 145°E

4. Fairbanks, Alaska
63°N, 148°W

5. Nairobi, Kenya
1°S, 37°E

6. London, England
50°N, 0°

7. Cape Town, South Africa
33°S, 18°E

8. Julianehab, Greenland
61°N, 46°W

9. La Paz, Bolivia
16°S, 68°W

Use a globe or world map to name the city located near each set of coordinates.

10. 34°S, 59°W
Buenos Aires, Argentina

11. 30°N, 90°W
New Orleans, Louisiana

12. 48°N, 123°W
Vancouver, Canada

13. 7°S, 107°E
Jakarta, Indonesia

14. 9°N, 38°E
Adis Abeba, Ethiopia

15. 51°N, 14°E
Berlin, Germany

16. 23°S, 46°W
São Paulo, Brazil

17. 18°N, 99°W
Mexico City, Mexico

18. 35°S, 173°E
Auckland, New Zealand

For each property listed from plane Euclidean geometry, write a corresponding statement for non-Euclidean spherical geometry.

19. Two lines intersecting to form four right angles are perpendicular. **Two great circles intersecting to form eight right angles are perpendicular.**

20. Through any two points in a plane there is a unique and infinite straight line. **Through any two points on a sphere there is a unique and finite great circle.**

21. An infinite number of lines can be drawn through a point in a plane. **An infinite number of great circles can be drawn through a point on a sphere.**

NAME_____ DATE _____

Practice

Classifying Triangles

For Exercises 1–7, refer to the figure at the right. Triangle ABC is isosceles with AB > AC and AB > BC. Also, $\overleftrightarrow{XY} \parallel \overline{AB}$. Name each of the following.

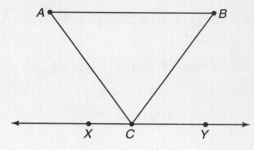

1. sides of the triangle

2. angles of the triangle

3. vertex angle

4. base angles

5. side opposite $\angle BCA$

6. congruent sides

7. angle opposite $\overline{AC}$

Use a protractor and ruler to draw triangles using the given conditions. Classify each triangle by the measures of its angles and sides.

8. $\triangle BHE$, $BE = 1$ inch, $m\angle E = 60$, $HE = \frac{1}{2}$ inch

9. $\triangle QTR$, $m\angle T = 60$, $QT = TR = 4$ cm

10. Find the measures of the legs of isosceles triangle ABC if $AB = 2x + 4$, $BC = 3x - 1$, $AC = x + 1$, and the perimeter of $\triangle ABC$ is 34 units.

4–1

NAME________________________________ DATE ____________

Practice

Student Edition
Pages 180–187

Classifying Triangles

For Exercises 1–7, refer to the figure at the right. Triangle ABC is isosceles with $AB > AC$ and $AB > BC$. Also, $\overleftrightarrow{XY} \parallel \overline{AB}$. Name each of the following.

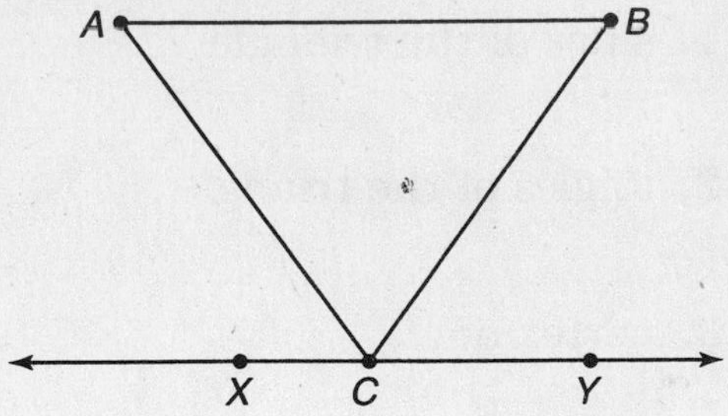

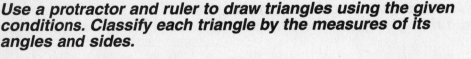

1. sides of the triangle **$\overline{AB}$, $\overline{BC}$, $\overline{AC}$**

2. angles of the triangle **$\angle A$, $\angle B$, $\angle ACB$**

3. vertex angle **$\angle ACB$**

4. base angles **$\angle A$, $\angle B$**

5. side opposite $\angle BCA$ **$\overline{AB}$**

6. congruent sides **$\overline{AC}$, $\overline{BC}$**

7. angle opposite $\overline{AC}$ **$\angle B$**

Use a protractor and ruler to draw triangles using the given conditions. Classify each triangle by the measures of its angles and sides.

8. $\triangle BHE$, $BE = 1$ inch, $m\angle E = 60$, $HE = \frac{1}{2}$ inch **right, scalene**

9. $\triangle QTR$, $m\angle T = 60$, $QT = TR = 4$ cm **equiangular, equilateral**

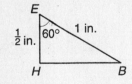

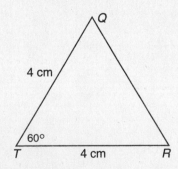

10. Find the measures of the legs of isosceles triangle ABC if $AB = 2x + 4$, $BC = 3x - 1$, $AC = x + 1$, and the perimeter of $\triangle ABC$ is 34 units. **14 units**

NAME_____ DATE _____

Practice

Student Edition
Pages 189–195

Measuring Angles in Triangles

Find the value of x.

1.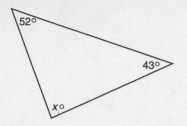

52°
43°
x°

2.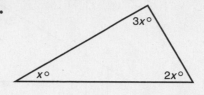

3x°
x°
2x°

3.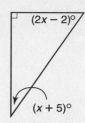

(2x − 2)°
(x + 5)°

4.

10°
x°
23°

5.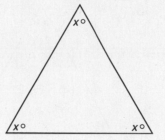

x°
x°
x°

6.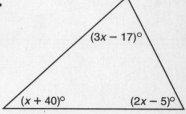

(3x − 17)°
(x + 40)°
(2x − 5)°

7.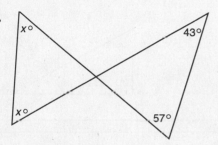

x°
43°
x°
57°

8.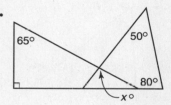

65°
50°
80°
x°

9.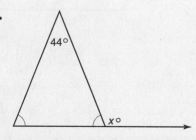

44°
x°

10.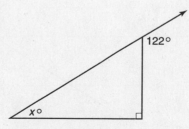

122°
x°

11.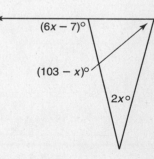

(6x − 7)°
(103 − x)°
2x°

12.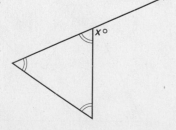

x°

13.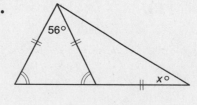

56°
x°

14.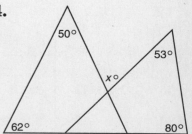

50°
53°
x°
62°
80°

21

4–2

Practice

Student Edition
Pages 189–195

Measuring Angles in Triangles

Find the value of x.

1.

52°

43°

x°

85

2.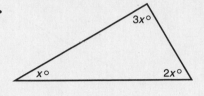

3x°

x°   2x°

30

3.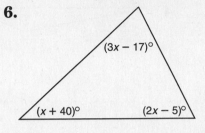

(2x − 2)°

(x + 5)°

29

4.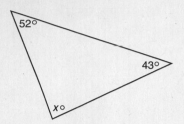

10°   x°   23°

147

5.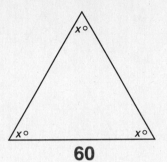

x°

x°   x°

60

6.

(3x − 17)°

(x + 40)°   (2x − 5)°

27

7.

x°   43°

x°   57°

50

8.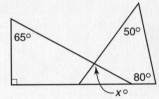

65°   50°

80°

x°

105

9.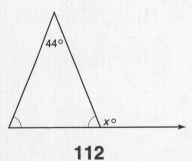

44°

x°

112

10.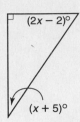

122°

x°

32

11.

(6x − 7)°

(103 − x)°

2x°

22

12.

x°

120

13.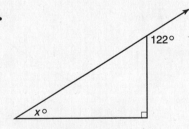

56°

x°

31

14.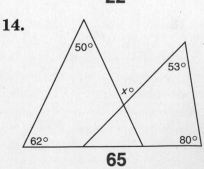

50°

53°

x°

62°   80°

65

Geometry

Practice

Exploring Congruent Triangles

Label the corresponding parts if △RST ≅ △ABC. Use the figures to complete each statement.

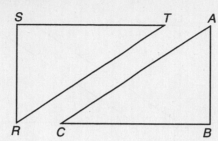

1. $\angle C \cong$ ___?___

2. $\angle R \cong$ ___?___

3. $\overline{AC} \cong$ ___?___

4. $\overline{ST} \cong$ ___?___

5. $\overline{RS} \cong$ ___?___

6. $\angle B \cong$ ___?___

Write a congruence statement for the congruent triangles in each diagram.

7.

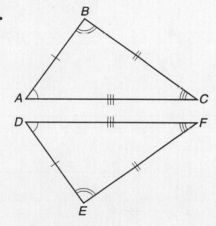

8.

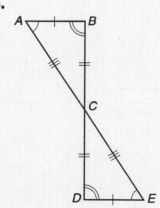

9. Given $\triangle ABC \cong \triangle DEF$, $AB = 15$, $BC = 20$, $AC = 25$, and $FE = 3x - 7$, find x.

10. Given $\triangle ABC \cong \triangle DEF$, $DE = 10$, $EF = 13$, $DF = 16$, and $AC = 4x - 8$, find x.

Geometry

Exploring Congruent Triangles

Label the corresponding parts if $\triangle RST \cong \triangle ABC$. Use the figures to complete each statement.

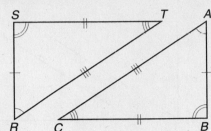

1. $\angle C \cong \underline{\ ?\ } \angle T$

2. $\angle R \cong \underline{\ ?\ } \angle A$

3. $\overline{AC} \cong \underline{\ ?\ } \overline{RT}$

4. $\overline{ST} \cong \underline{\ ?\ } \overline{BC}$

5. $\overline{RS} \cong \underline{\ ?\ } \overline{AB}$

6. $\angle B \cong \underline{\ ?\ } \angle S$

Write a congruence statement for the congruent triangles in each diagram. **Sample triangle names are given.**

7.

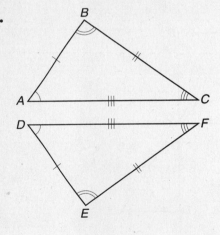

$\triangle ABC \cong \triangle DEF$

8.

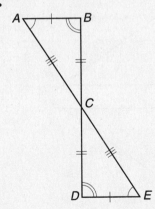

$\triangle ACB \cong \triangle ECD$

9. Given $\triangle ABC \cong \triangle DEF$, $AB = 15$, $BC = 20$, $AC = 25$, and $FE = 3x - 7$, find x. **9**

10. Given $\triangle ABC \cong \triangle DEF$, $DE = 10$, $EF = 13$, $DF = 16$, and $AC = 4x - 8$, find x. **6**

Practice

Proving Triangles Congruent

For each figure, mark all congruent parts. Then complete the
prove statement and identify the postulate that can be used to
prove the triangles congruent.

1.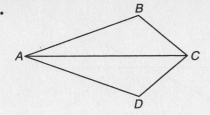

2.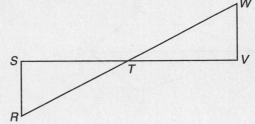

Given: $\overline{AB} \cong \overline{AD}$
$\overline{BC} \cong \overline{DC}$

Prove: $\triangle BCA \cong \underline{\ ?\ }$

Given: $\angle S$ and $\angle V$ are right angles.
T bisects $\overline{SV}$.

Prove: $\triangle RST \cong \underline{\ ?\ }$

Write a two-column proof.

3. **Given:** $\overline{BD} \perp \overline{AC}$
D bisects $\overline{AC}$.

Prove: $\overline{AB} \cong \overline{CB}$

Proof:

Statements	Reasons

4. **Given:** $\angle 2 \cong \angle 1$
$\angle 4 \cong \angle 5$

Prove: $\overline{BC} \cong \overline{DC}$

Proof:

Statements	Reasons

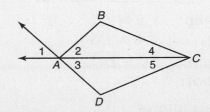

Geometry

NAME_____ DATE _____

Practice

Proving Triangles Congruent

For each figure, mark all congruent parts. Then complete the prove statement and identify the postulate that can be used to prove the triangles congruent.

1.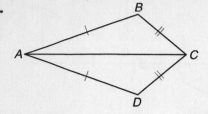

2.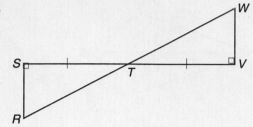

Given: $\overline{AB} \cong \overline{AD}$
$\overline{BC} \cong \overline{DC}$

Prove: $\triangle BCA \cong$ __?__ $\triangle DCA$; **SSS**

Given: $\angle S$ and $\angle V$ are right angles.
T bisects $\overline{SV}$.

Prove: $\triangle RST \cong$ __?__ $\triangle WVT$; **ASA**

Write a two-column proof.

3. **Given:** $\overline{BD} \perp \overline{AC}$
D bisects $\overline{AC}$.

Prove: $\overline{AB} \cong \overline{CB}$
Proof:

Statements	Reasons
a. D bisects $\overline{AC}$	a. Given
b. $\overline{AD} \cong \overline{CD}$	b. Definition of bisector
c. $\overline{BD} \perp \overline{AC}$	c. Given
d. $\angle ADB$ and $\angle CDB$ are right $\triangle$.	d. $\perp$ lines form 4 rt. $\triangle$.
e. $\angle ADB \cong \angle CDB$	e. All rt. $\triangle$ are $\cong$.
f. $\overline{BD} \cong \overline{BD}$	f. Congruence of segments is reflexive.
g. $\triangle ADB \cong \triangle CBD$	g. SAS
h. $\overline{AB} \cong \overline{CB}$	h. CPCTC

4. **Given:** $\angle 2 \cong \angle 1$
$\angle 4 \cong \angle 5$

Prove: $\overline{BC} \cong \overline{DC}$
Proof:

Statements	Reasons
a. $\angle 2 \cong \angle 1$	a. Given
b. $\angle 1 \cong \angle 3$	b. Vert. $\triangle$ are $\cong$.
c. $\angle 2 \cong \angle 3$	c. Congruence of $\triangle$ is transitive.
d. $\overline{AC} \cong \overline{AC}$	d. Congruence of segments is reflexive.
e. $\angle 4 \cong \angle 5$	e. Given
f. $\triangle ABC \cong \triangle ADC$	f. ASA
g. $\overline{BC} \cong \overline{DC}$	g. CPCTC

Geometry

NAME _____ DATE _____

Practice

More Congruent Triangles

Draw and label triangles MNO and XYZ. Indicate the additional pairs of corresponding parts that would have to be proved congruent in order to use the given postulate or theorem to prove the triangles congruent.

1. $\angle N \cong \angle Y$ and $\overline{NO} \cong \overline{YZ}$ by ASA

2. $\angle O \cong \angle Z$ and $\angle M \cong \angle X$ by AAS

3. $\angle O \cong \angle Z$ and $\overline{MO} \cong \overline{XZ}$ by AAS

4. $\angle N \cong \angle Y$ and $\angle M \cong \angle X$ by ASA

5. The statements in the following proof are *not* in logical order. Rearrange them in a correct sequence and give the reasons.

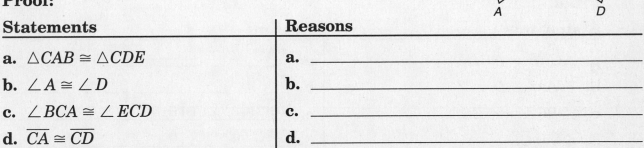

Given: $\angle A \cong \angle D$
$\overline{AB} \cong \overline{DE}$
Prove: $\overline{CA} \cong \overline{CD}$
Proof:

Statements	Reasons
a. $\triangle CAB \cong \triangle CDE$	**a.** _____
b. $\angle A \cong \angle D$	**b.** _____
c. $\angle BCA \cong \angle ECD$	**c.** _____
d. $\overline{CA} \cong \overline{CD}$	**d.** _____
e. $\overline{BA} \cong \overline{ED}$	**e.** _____

6. Eliminate the Possibilities Barky, Spot, and Tiger are dogs. One is a black labrador retriever, one is a multi-colored collie, and one is a spotted dalmatian. One is owned by a doctor, one is owned by a lawyer, and one is owned by an insurance salesperson. The lawyer's dog does not have spots. The doctor's dog has more than one color. The insurance salesperson's dog is solid in color. Who owns which dog?

NAME______________________ DATE ____________

Practice

Student Edition
Pages 214–221

More Congruent Triangles

Draw and label triangles MNO and XYZ. Indicate the additional pairs of corresponding parts that would have to be proved congruent in order to use the given postulate or theorem to prove the triangles congruent.

1. $\angle N \cong \angle Y$ and $\overline{NO} \cong \overline{YZ}$ by ASA

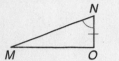

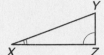

$\angle O \cong \angle Z$

2. $\angle O \cong \angle Z$ and $\angle M \cong \angle X$ by AAS

$\angle \overline{NO} \cong \overline{YZ}$ or $\overline{MN} \cong \overline{XY}$

3. $\angle O \cong \angle Z$ and $\overline{MO} \cong \overline{XZ}$ by AAS

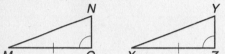

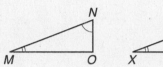

$\angle N \cong \angle Y$

4. $\angle N \cong \angle Y$ and $\angle M \cong \angle X$ by ASA

$\overline{MN} \cong \overline{XY}$

5. The statements in the following proof are *not* in logical order. Rearrange them in a correct sequence and give the reasons.

Given: $\angle A \cong \angle D$
$\overline{AB} \cong \overline{DE}$
Prove: $\overline{CA} \cong \overline{CD}$
Proof:

One order of steps: b, c, e, a, d

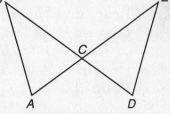

Statements	Reasons
a. $\triangle CAB \cong \triangle CDE$	**a.** **AAS**
b. $\angle A \cong \angle D$	**b.** **Given**
c. $\angle BCA \cong \angle ECD$	**c.** **Vertical $\angle$s are $\cong$.**
d. $\overline{CA} \cong \overline{CD}$	**d.** **CPCTC**
e. $\overline{BA} \cong \overline{ED}$	**e.** **Given**

6. Eliminate the Possibilities Barky, Spot, and Tiger are dogs. One is a black labrador retriever, one is a multi-colored collie, and one is a spotted dalmatian. One is owned by a doctor, one is owned by a lawyer, and one is owned by an insurance salesperson. The lawyer's dog does not have spots. The doctor's dog has more than one color. The insurance salesperson's dog is solid in color. Who owns which dog?
doctor—dalmatian; lawyer—collie; insurance salesperson—labrador retriever

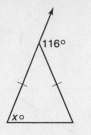

Practice

Student Edition
Pages 222–228

Analyzing Isosceles Triangles

Find the value of x.

1.

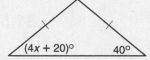

116°

x°

2.

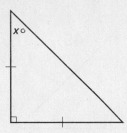

x°

3.

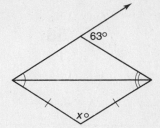

63°

x°

4.

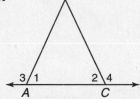

(4x + 20)°   40°

5.

(4x + 10)°

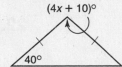

40°

6.

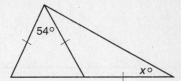

54°

x°

Write a two-column proof.

7. **Given:** ∠3 ≅ ∠4
   Prove: $\overline{AB} \cong \overline{BC}$
   Proof:

B

3/1   2\4
A   C

Statements	Reasons

8. **Given:** $\overline{AR} \cong \overline{AQ}$
   $\overline{RS} \cong \overline{QT}$
   Prove: $\overline{AS} \cong \overline{AT}$
   Proof:

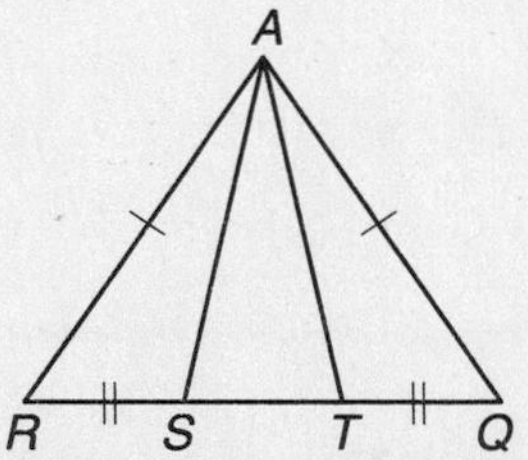

A

R   S   T   Q

Statements	Reasons

Geometry

NAME______________________________ DATE __________

4–6

Practice

Student Edition
Pages 222–228

Analyzing Isosceles Triangles

Find the value of x.

1. 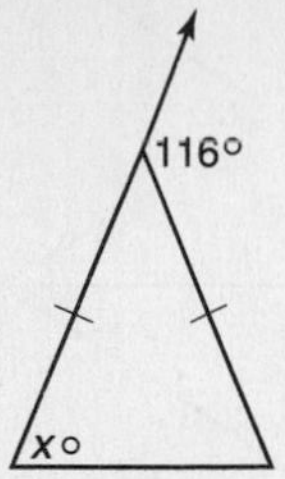

58

2. 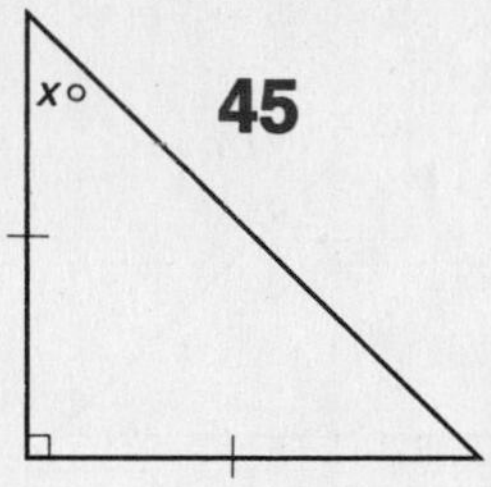

45

3. 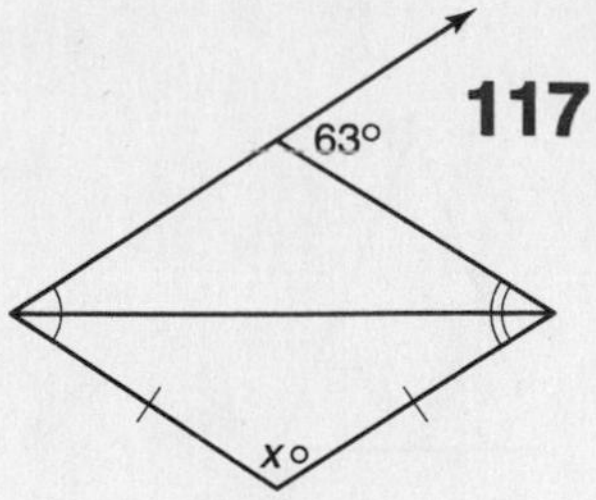

117

4. 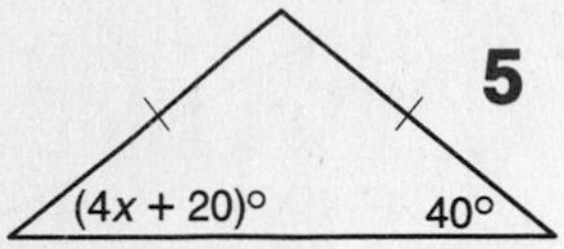

5

5. 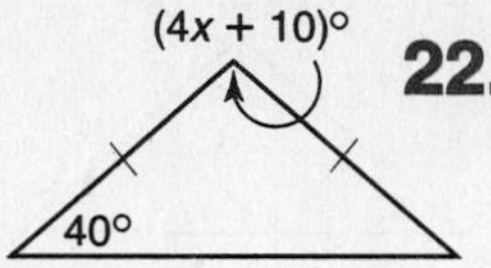

22.5

6. 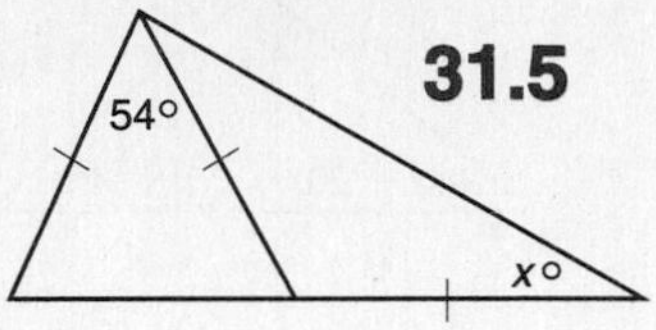

31.5

Write a two-column proof.

7. Given: $\angle 3 \cong \angle 4$
Prove: $\overline{AB} \cong \overline{BC}$
Proof:

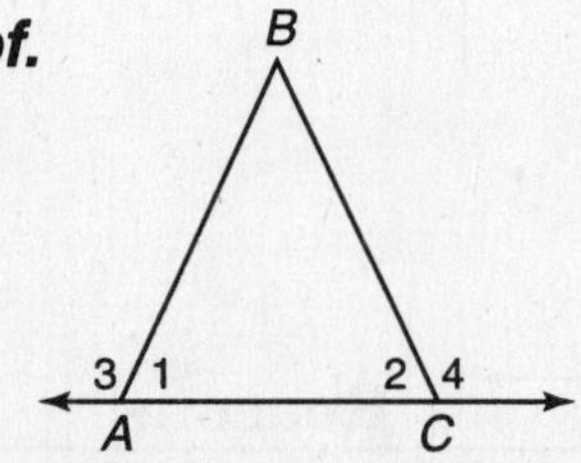

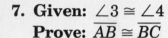

Statements	**Reasons**
a. $\angle 3 \cong \angle 4$	a. Given
b. $\angle 3$ and $\angle 1$ form a linear pair. $\angle 4$ and $\angle 2$ form a linear pair.	b. Definition of linear pair.
c. $\angle 3$ and $\angle 1$ are supplementary. $\angle 4$ and $\angle 2$ are supplementary.	c. If 2 ∠s form a linear pair, they are supp.
d. $\angle 3 \cong \angle 4$	d. ∠s supp. to ≅ ∠s are ≅.
e. $AB \cong BC$	e. If 2 ∠s of a △ are ≅, the sides opp. the ∠s are ≅.

8. Given: $\overline{AR} \cong \overline{AQ}$
$\overline{RS} \cong \overline{QT}$
Prove: $\overline{AS} \cong \overline{AT}$
Proof:

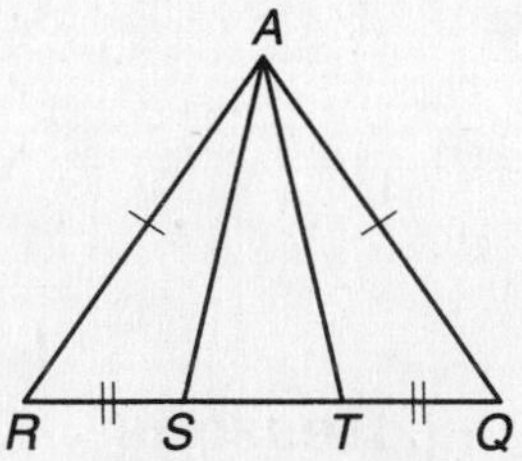

Statements	**Reasons**
a. $\overline{AR} \cong \overline{AQ}$	a. Given
b. $\angle R \cong \angle Q$	b. If 2 sides of a △ are ≅, the ∠s opp. the sides are ≅.
c. $\overline{RS} \cong \overline{QT}$	c. Given
d. $\triangle ARS \cong \triangle AQT$	d. SAS
e. $\overline{AS} \cong \overline{AT}$	e. CPCTC

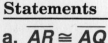

NAME_____ DATE_____

Practice

Special Segments in Triangles

1. Find AB if $\overline{BD}$ is a median of $\triangle ABC$.

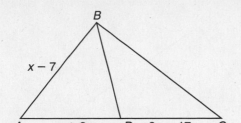

2. Find BC if $\overline{AD}$ is an altitude of $\triangle ABC$.

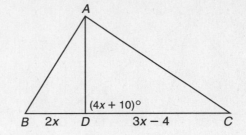

3. Find $m\angle ABC$ if $\overline{BD}$ is an angle bisector of $\triangle ABC$.

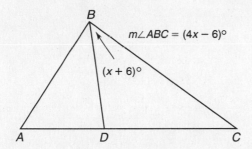

In Exercises 4–6, A(2, 5), B(12, -1), and C(-6, 8) are the vertices of △ABC.

4. What are the coordinates of K if $\overline{CK}$ is a median of $\triangle ABC$?

5. What is the slope of the perpendicular bisector of $\overline{AB}$? What is the slope of $\overline{CL}$ if $\overline{CL}$ is the altitude from point C?

6. Point N on $\overleftrightarrow{BC}$ has coordinates $\left(\frac{8}{5}, \frac{21}{5}\right)$. Is $\overline{NA}$ an altitude of $\triangle ABC$? Explain your answer.

26

Special Segments in Triangles

1. Find AB if $\overline{BD}$ is a median of $\triangle ABC$.
13

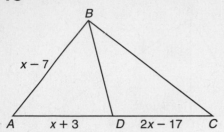

2. Find BC if $\overline{AD}$ is an altitude of $\triangle ABC$.
96

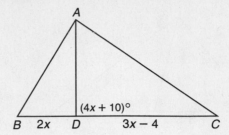

3. Find $m\angle ABC$ if $\overline{BD}$ is an angle bisector of $\triangle ABC$. **30**

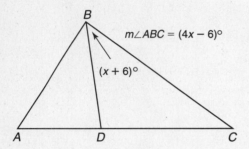

In Exercises 4–6, A(2, 5), B(12, -1), and C(-6, 8) are the vertices of △ ABC.

4. What are the coordinates of K if $\overline{CK}$ is a median of $\triangle ABC$? **(7, 2)**

5. What is the slope of the perpendicular bisector of $\overline{AB}$? What is the slope of $\overline{CL}$ if $\overline{CL}$ is the altitude from point C?
$\dfrac{5}{3}, \dfrac{5}{3}$

6. Point N on $\overleftrightarrow{BC}$ has coordinates $\left(\dfrac{8}{5}, \dfrac{21}{5}\right)$. Is $\overline{NA}$ an altitude of $\triangle ABC$? Explain your answer.
Yes; N is on the line that contains $\overline{BC}$, and the product of the slope of $\overline{BC}$, $-\dfrac{1}{2}$, and the slope of $\overline{AN}$, 2, is -1.

Right Triangles

For each figure, find the values of x and y so that
△ DEF ≅ △ PQR by the indicated theorem or postulate.

1. HA

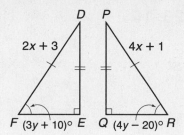

2. LL

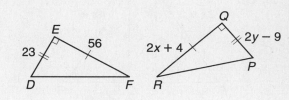

3. LA

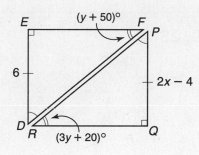

4. HL

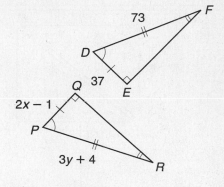

5. Write a two-column proof.
   Given: $\overline{AB}$ bisects $\angle DAC$
   $\angle C$ and $\angle D$ are right angles.
   Prove: $\overline{BC} \cong \overline{BD}$
   Proof:

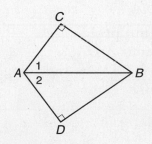

Statements	**Reasons**

Right Triangles

For each figure, find the values of x and y so that
△ DEF ≅ △ PQR by the indicated theorem or postulate.

1. HA
2, 30

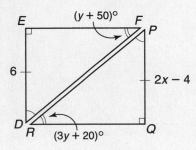

2. LL **26, 16**

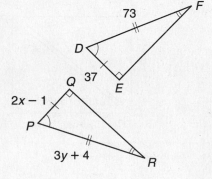

3. LA
5, 15

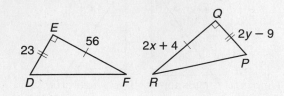

4. HL
19, 23

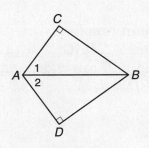

5. Write a two-column proof.
   Given: $\overline{AB}$ bisects $\angle DAC$
   $\angle C$ and $\angle D$ are right angles.
   Prove: $\overline{BC} \cong \overline{BD}$
   Proof:

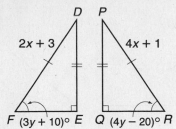

Statements	Reasons
a. *AB* bisects $\angle DAC$.	a. Given
b. $\angle 1 \cong \angle 2$	b. Definition of bisector
c. $\angle C$ and $\angle D$ are right angles.	c. Given
d. $\triangle ACB$ and $\triangle ADB$ are right triangles.	d. Definition of right triangle
e. $\overline{AB} \cong \overline{AB}$	e. Congruence of segments is reflexive.
f. $\triangle ACB \cong \triangle ADB$	f. HA
g. $\overline{BC} \cong \overline{BD}$	g. CPCTC

Indirect Proof and Inequalities

*Use the figure at the right to complete each statement with
either < or >.*

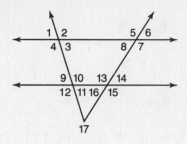

1. $\angle 4$ _?_ $\angle 8$

2. $\angle 13$ _?_ $\angle 11$

3. $\angle 17$ _?_ $\angle 8$

4. If $m\angle 15 = m\angle 7$ then $m\angle 11$ _?_ $m\angle 7$.

Write an indirect proof.

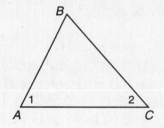

5. **Given:** $m\angle 1 \neq m\angle 2$
   Prove: $\triangle ABC$ is not an isosceles
   triangle with vertex B.

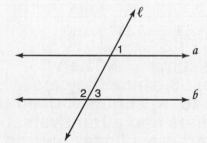

6. **Given:** $m\angle 1 + m\angle 2 \neq 180$
   Prove: $a \nparallel b$

7. **Work Backward** Joe spent half of the money in his wallet
   on a table for his computer printer. He then spent $8.12 for a
   printer ribbon. Then he spent half of what he had left on
   supplies for his office. He then had $14.50 remaining. How
   much money did Joe have to start with?

NAME_____ DATE _____

Practice

Student Edition
Pages 252–258

Indirect Proof and Inequalities

Use the figure at the right to complete each statement with either < or >.

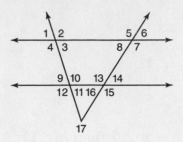

1. $\angle 4 \underline{\ ?\ } \angle 8$ >

2. $\angle 13 \underline{\ ?\ } \angle 11$ >

3. $\angle 17 \underline{\ ?\ } \angle 8$ <

4. If $m\angle 15 = m\angle 7$ then $m\angle 11 \underline{\ ?\ } m\angle 7.$ <

Write an indirect proof.

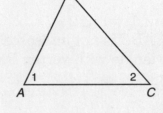

5. **Given:** $m\angle 1 \neq m\angle 2$
   Prove: $\triangle ABC$ is not an isosceles triangle with vertex B.
   Proof: Assume $\triangle ABC$ is isosceles, with vertex B. Then $AB = BC$ by the definition of isosceles triangle. This implies that $m\angle 1 = m\angle 2$, since angles opposite congruent sides of a triangle are congruent. This contradicts the given information. Therefore, $\triangle ABC$ cannot be an isosceles triangle with vertex B.

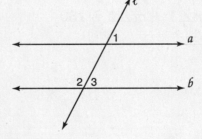

6. **Given:** $m\angle 1 + m\angle 2 \neq 180$
   Prove: $a \not\parallel b$
   Proof: Assume $a \parallel b$. Then $m\angle 1 = m\angle 3$, since they are corresponding angles formed by parallel lines and a transversal. $\angle 2$ and $\angle 3$ are a linear pair, so $m\angle 2 + m\angle 3 = 180$. By substitution, $m\angle 2 + m\angle 1 = 180$. This contradicts given information. Therefore, $a \not\parallel b$.

7. **Work Backward** Joe spent half of the money in his wallet on a table for his computer printer. He then spent $8.12 for a printer ribbon. Then he spent half of what he had left on supplies for his office. He then had $14.50 remaining. How much money did Joe have to start with? **$74.24**

Practice

Inequalities for Sides and Angles of a Triangle

Refer to the figure on the right for Exercises 1–4.

1. Name the shortest and the longest segments in △*BCD*.

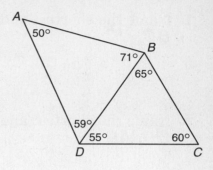

2. Name the shortest and the longest segments in △*ABD*.

3. Find the shortest segment in the figure.

4. How many of the segments in the figure are longer than $\overline{BD}$?

5. List the angles in order from least to greatest.

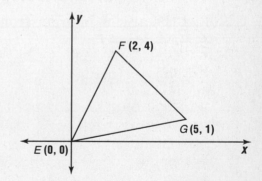

6. List the sides of △*MNO* in order from longest to shortest if $m\angle M = 4x + 20$, $m\angle N = 2x + 10$, and $m\angle O = 3x - 20$.

7. List the angles of △*KLM* in order from least to greatest if $KL = x - 4$, $LM = x + 4$, $KM = 2x - 1$, and the perimeter of △*KLM* is 27.

Practice

Student Edition
Pages 259–265

Inequalities for Sides and Angles of a Triangle

Refer to the figure on the right for Exercises 1–4.

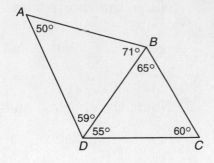

1. Name the shortest and the longest segments in △BCD.
   BC, DC

2. Name the shortest and the longest segments in △ABD.
   BD, AD

3. Find the shortest segment in the figure. $\overline{BC}$

4. How many of the segments in the figure are longer than $\overline{BD}$? **3**

5. List the angles in order from least to greatest.
   ∠E, ∠G, ∠F

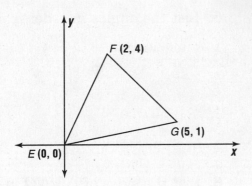

6. List the sides of △MNO in order from longest to shortest if $m\angle M = 4x + 20$, $m\angle N = 2x + 10$, and $m\angle O = 3x - 20$. **NO, MO, MN**

7. List the angles of △KLM in order from least to greatest if $KL = x - 4$, $LM = x + 4$, $KM = 2x - 1$, and the perimeter of △KLM is 27. **∠M, ∠K, ∠L**

NAME_____ DATE _____

Practice

The Triangle Inequality

Determine whether it is possible to draw a triangle with sides of the given measure. Write yes or no.

1. 3, 3, 3

2. 2, 3, 4

3. 1, 2, 3

4. 8.9, 9.3, 18.3

5. 16.5, 20.5, 38.5

6. 19, 19, 0.5

Determine whether it is possible to have a triangle with the given vertices. Write yes or no, and explain your answer.

7. $A(-2, -2)$, $B(-1, 1)$, $C(1, 4)$

8. $A(-4, 2)$, $B(-2, 1)$, $C(2, -1)$

9. $A(2, 5)$, $B(-3, 5)$, $C(6, -1)$

10. $A(3, -6)$, $B(1, 2)$, $C(-2, 10)$

Two sides of a triangle are 21 and 24 inches long. Determine whether each measurement can be the length of the third side.

11. 3 inches

12. 40 inches

13. 56 inches

If the sides of a triangle have the following lengths, find all possible values for x.

14. $AB = 2x + 5$, $BC = 3x - 2$, $AC = 4x - 8$

15. $PQ = 3x$, $QR = 4x - 7$, $PR = 2x + 9$

30

Practice

The Triangle Inequality

Determine whether it is possible to draw a triangle with sides of the given measure. Write yes or no.

1. 3, 3, 3 **yes**

2. 2, 3, 4 **yes**

3. 1, 2, 3 **no**

4. 8.9, 9.3, 18.3 **no**

5. 16.5, 20.5, 38.5 **no**

6. 19, 19, 0.5 **yes**

Determine whether it is possible to have a triangle with the given vertices. Write yes or no, and explain your answer.

7. $A(-2, -2)$, $B(-1, 1)$, $C(1, 4)$
 Yes; $AB = \sqrt{10}$, $BC = \sqrt{13}$, $AC = 3\sqrt{5}$ **and all triangle inequalities are satisfied.**

8. $A(-4, 2)$, $B(-2, 1)$, $C(2, -1)$
 no; $AB = \sqrt{5}$, $BC = 2\sqrt{5}$, $AC = 3\sqrt{5}$
 $AB + BC = AC$

9. $A(2, 5)$, $B(-3, 5)$, $C(6, -1)$
 yes; $AB = 5$, $BC = 3\sqrt{13}$, $AC = 2\sqrt{13}$ **and all triangle inequalities are satisfied.**

10. $A(3, -6)$, $B(1, 2)$, $C(-2, 10)$
 yes; $AB = 2\sqrt{17}$, $BC = \sqrt{73}$, $AC = \sqrt{281}$ **and all triangle inequalities are satisfied.**

Two sides of a triangle are 21 and 24 inches long. Determine whether each measurement can be the length of the third side.

11. 3 inches **no**

12. 40 inches **yes**

13. 56 inches **no**

If the sides of a triangle have the following lengths, find all possible values for x.

14. $AB = 2x + 5$, $BC = 3x - 2$, $AC = 4x - 8$
 $\{x \mid x > 3\}$

15. $PQ = 3x$, $QR = 4x - 7$, $PR = 2x + 9$
 $\left\{x \mid x > \dfrac{16}{5}\right\}$

NAME _____ DATE _____

Practice

Inequalities Involving Two Triangles

Refer to each figure to write an inequality relating the given pair of angle measures.

1. $m\angle PRQ, m\angle PRS$

2. $m\angle ABE, m\angle DBC$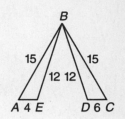

Write an inequality or pair of inequalities to describe the possible values of x.

3.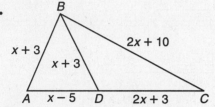

4.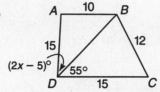

Write a two-column proof.

5. **Given:** $\overline{AD} \cong \overline{EC}$
   $m\angle ADC > m\angle ECD$
   Prove: $AC > ED$
   Proof:

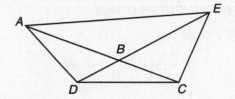

Statements	Reasons

6. **Given:** D is the midpoint of $\overline{AC}$.
   $BC > AB$
   Prove: $m\angle 1 > m\angle 2$
   Proof:

Statements	Reasons

Geometry

Inequalities Involving Two Triangles

Refer to each figure to write an inequality relating the given pair of angle measures.

1. $m\angle PRQ, m\angle PRS$

$$m\angle PRQ < m\angle PRS$$

2. $m\angle ABE, m\angle DBC$

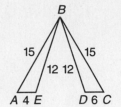

$$m\angle ABE < m\angle DBC$$

Write an inequality or pair of inequalities to describe the possible values of x.

3.

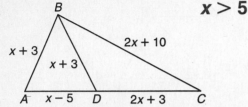

$x > 5$

4.

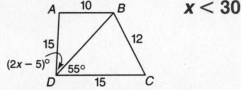

$x < 30$

Write a two-column proof.

5. Given: $\overline{AD} \cong \overline{EC}$
$m\angle ADC > m\angle ECD$
Prove: $AC > ED$
Proof:

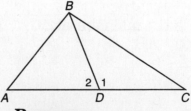

Statements	Reasons
a. $AD \cong EC$	a. Given
b. $DC \cong DC$	b. Congruence of segments is reflexive.
c. $m\angle ADC > m\angle ECD$	c. Given
d. $AC > ED$	d. SAS inequality

6. Given: D is the midpoint of $\overline{AC}$.
$BC > AB$
Prove: $m\angle 1 > m\angle 2$
Proof:

Statements	Reasons
a. D is the midpoint of $\overline{AC}$.	a. Given
b. $\overline{AD} \cong \overline{DC}$	b. Definition of midpoint
c. $BD \cong BD$	c. Congruence of segments is reflexive.
d. $\overline{BC} > \overline{AB}$	d. Given
e. $m\angle 1 > m\angle 2$	e. SSS Inequality

Practice

Parallelograms

The figure at the right is a parallelogram. Use this figure and the information given to solve each problem.

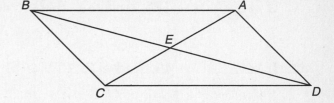

1. If $m\angle BCD = 125$, find $m\angle BAD$.

2. If $m\angle BAC = 45$, find $m\angle ACD$.

3. If $m\angle BEA = 135$, find $m\angle AED$.

4. If $m\angle ABC = 50$, find $m\angle BCD$.

5. If $AB = 5x - 3$ and $CD = 2x + 9$, find AB.

6. If $m\angle DAB = 2x - 10$ and $m\angle ADC = 3x$, find $m\angle DAB$.

7. If $m\angle BAD = 3x - 12$ and $m\angle BDC = x + 40$, find $m\angle BAD$.

8. Write a two-column proof.
   Given: $ABCD$ is a parallelogram, $\overline{BE} \cong \overline{AD}$
   Prove: $\angle 1 \cong \angle C$

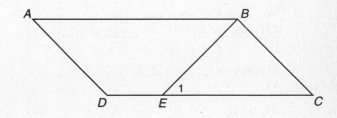

   Proof:

Statements	Reasons

Parallelograms

The figure at the right is a parallelogram. Use this figure and the information given to solve each problem.

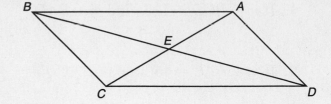

1. If $m\angle BCD = 125$, find $m\angle BAD$. **125**

2. If $m\angle BAC = 45$, find $m\angle ACD$. **45**

3. If $m\angle BEA = 135$, find $m\angle AED$. **45**

4. If $m\angle ABC = 50$, find $m\angle BCD$. **130**

5. If $AB = 5x - 3$ and $CD = 2x + 9$, find AB. **17**

6. If $m\angle DAB = 2x - 10$ and $m\angle ADC = 3x$, find $m\angle DAB$. **66**

7. If $m\angle BAD = 3x - 12$ and $m\angle BDC = x + 40$, find $m\angle BAD$. **66**

8. Write a two-column proof.
   Given: $ABCD$ is a parallelogram, $\overline{BE} \cong \overline{AD}$
   Prove: $\angle 1 \cong \angle C$

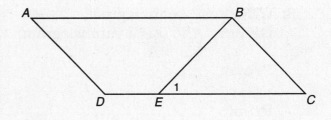

   Proof:

Statements	Reasons
a. $ABCD$ is a parallelogram.	a. Given
b. $\overline{AD} \cong \overline{BC}$	b. Opposite sides of a parallelogram are congruent.
c. $\overline{BE} \cong \overline{AD}$	c. Given
d. $\overline{BC} \cong \overline{BE}$	d. Congruence of segments is transitive.
e. $\angle 1 \cong \angle C$	e. If two sides of a triangle are congruent, then the angles opposite those sides are congruent.

NAME_____ DATE _____

Practice

Tests for Parallelograms

Find the values of x and y that insure each quadrilateral is a parallelogram.

1.

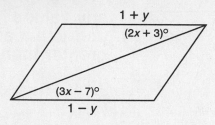

2.

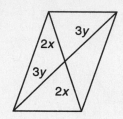

3. Refer to the figure at the right. $\overline{YZ}$
   bisects $\angle XYK$ and $\overline{LK}$ bisects
   $\angle ZLM$. Also, $\angle 1 \cong \angle 2$.
   Is $YZLK$ a parallelogram? Explain.

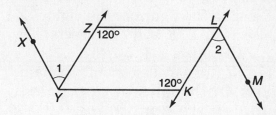

4. Refer to the figure at the right.
   $\overline{AC} \cong \overline{WV}$ and $\overline{BD} \cong \overline{WV}$. Also,
   $\overline{AB} \cong \overline{XY}$ and $\overline{CD} \cong \overline{XY}$. Is $ABCD$ a
   parallelogram? Explain.

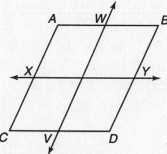

Determine whether quadrilateral ABCD with the given vertices is a parallelogram. Explain.

5. $A(2, 5)$, $B(5, 9)$, $C(3, -1)$, $D(6, 3)$

6. $A(-1, 6)$, $B(2, -3)$, $C(5, 9)$, $D(2, 7)$

7. **Identify Subgoals** Identify the subgoals you would need to
   accomplish to complete the proof.

   Given: $\overline{YN} \perp \overline{XZ}, \overline{ZM} \perp \overline{XY}$
   $\overline{XZ} \cong \overline{XY}$
   $\overline{XM} \cong \overline{XN}$

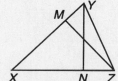

Practice

Tests for Parallelograms

Find the values of x and y that insure each quadrilateral is a parallelogram.

1.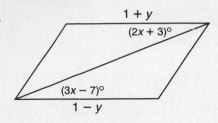
   $(2x + 3)°$
   $1 + y$
   $(3x − 7)°$
   $1 − y$

   10,0

2.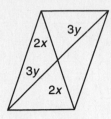
   $2x$ $3y$
   $3y$ $2x$

   **any values for x
   and y that are
   greater than 0**

3. Refer to the figure at the right. $\overline{YZ}$
   bisects $\angle XYK$ and $\overline{LK}$ bisects
   $\angle ZLM$. Also, $\angle 1 \cong \angle 2$.
   Is YZLK a parallelogram? Explain.
   **Yes, both pairs of opposite
   angles are congruent.**

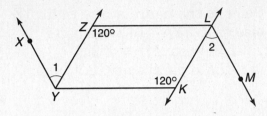

4. Refer to the figure at the right.
   $\overline{AC} \cong \overline{WV}$ and $\overline{BD} \cong \overline{WV}$. Also,
   $\overline{AB} \cong \overline{XY}$ and $\overline{CD} \cong \overline{XY}$. Is ABCD a
   parallelogram? Explain. **Yes, both
   pairs of opposite sides are
   congruent.**

**Determine whether quadrilateral ABCD with the given vertices
is a parallelogram. Explain.**

5. $A(2, 5)$, $B(5, 9)$, $C(3, -1)$, $D(6, 3)$ **Yes, opposite sides
   have equal lengths and are therefore congruent.**

6. $A(-1, 6)$, $B(2, -3)$, $C(5, 9)$, $D(2, 7)$ **No, slope**

   $\overline{AD} = \dfrac{1}{3}$ **and slope** $\overline{BC} = 4$**, so these two opposite
   sides are not parallel.**

7. **Identify Subgoals**   Identify the subgoals you would need to
   accomplish to complete the proof.

   Given: $\overline{YN} \perp \overline{XZ}$, $\overline{ZM} \perp \overline{XY}$
   $\overline{XZ} \cong \overline{XY}$
   $\overline{XM} \cong \overline{XN}$

   Subgoals: $\triangle XZM \cong \triangle XYN$, $\angle XMZ \cong \angle XNY$

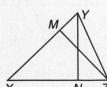

Practice

Rectangles

Use rectangle ABCD and the given information to solve each problem.

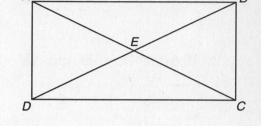

1. If $AC = 4x - 60$ and $BD = 30 - x$, find BD.

2. If $AC = 4x - 60$ and $AE = x + 5$, find EC.

3. If $m\angle BAC = 4x + 5$ and $m\angle CAD = 5x - 14$, find $m\angle CAD$.

4. If $AE = 2x + 3$ and $BE = 12 - x$, find BD.

5. If $m\angle BAC = 3x + 5$ and $m\angle ACD = 40 - 2x$. Find $m\angle AED$.

Determine whether PQRS is a rectangle. Justify your answer.

6. $P(2, 3)$, $Q(5, 9)$, $R(11, 6)$, $S(8, 0)$

7. $P(-1, 4)$, $Q(3, 6)$, $R(9, -3)$, $S(5, -5)$

8. $P(1, 3)$, $Q(4, 7)$, $R(6, 2)$, $S(2, 4)$

9. $P(-1, -3)$, $Q(-4, 6)$, $R(8, 10)$, $S(11, 1)$

10. $P(-1, -2)$, $Q(5, 2)$, $R(13, -10)$, $S(7, -14)$

Rectangles

Use rectangle ABCD and the given information to solve each problem.

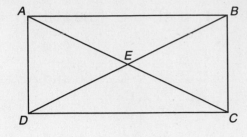

1. If $AC = 4x - 60$ and $BD = 30 - x$, find BD. **12**

2. If $AC = 4x - 60$ and $AE = x + 5$, find EC. **40**

3. If $m\angle BAC = 4x + 5$ and $m\angle CAD = 5x - 14$, find $m\angle CAD$. **41**

4. If $AE = 2x + 3$ and $BE = 12 - x$, find BD. **18**

5. If $m\angle BAC = 3x + 5$ and $m\angle ACD = 40 - 2x$. Find $m\angle AED$. **52**

Determine whether PQRS is a rectangle. Justify your answer.

6. $P(2, 3)$, $Q(5, 9)$, $R(11, 6)$, $S(8, 0)$ **yes; opposite sides parallel and all right angles**

7. $P(-1, 4)$, $Q(3, 6)$, $R(9, -3)$, $S(5, -5)$ **no; not all right angles**

8. $P(1, 3)$, $Q(4, 7)$, $R(6, 2)$, $S(2, 4)$ **no; opposite sides not parallel**

9. $P(-1, -3)$, $Q(-4, 6)$, $R(8, 10)$, $S(11, 1)$ **yes; opposite sides parallel and all right angles**

10. $P(-1, -2)$, $Q(5, 2)$, $R(13, -10)$, $S(7, -14)$ **yes; opposite sides parallel and all right angles**

Practice

Squares and Rhombi

Use square ABCD and the given information to find each value.

1. If $m\angle AEB = 3x$, find x.

2. If $m\angle BAC = 9x$, find x.

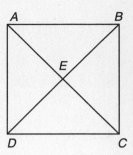

3. If $AB = 2x + 4$ and $CD = 3x - 5$, find BC.

4. If $m\angle DAC = y$ and $m\angle BAC = 3x$, find x.

5. If $AB = x^2 - 15$ and $BC = 2x$, find x.

Use rhombus ABCD and the given information to find each measure.

6. $m\angle BCE$

7. $m\angle BEC$

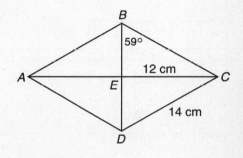

8. AC

9. $m\angle ABD$

10. AD

Determine whether EFGH is a parallelogram, a rectangle, a rhombus, or a square for each set of vertices. List all that apply.

11. $E(0, -3)$, $F(-3, 0)$, $G(0, 3)$, $H(3, 0)$

12. $E(2, 1)$, $F(3, 4)$, $G(7, 2)$, $H(6, -1)$

6–4

Practice

Squares and Rhombi

Use square ABCD and the given information to find each value.

1. If $m\angle AEB = 3x$, find x. **30**

2. If $m\angle BAC = 9x$, find x. **5**

3. If $AB = 2x + 4$ and $CD = 3x - 5$, find BC. **22**

4. If $m\angle DAC = y$ and $m\angle BAC = 3x$, find x. **15**

5. If $AB = x^2 - 15$ and $BC = 2x$, find x. **5**

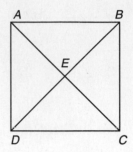

Use rhombus ABCD and the given information to find each measure.

6. $m\angle BCE$ **31**

7. $m\angle BEC$ **90**

8. AC **24 cm**

9. $m\angle ABD$ **59**

10. AD **14 cm**

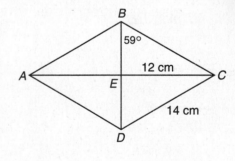

Determine whether EFGH is a parallelogram, a rectangle, a rhombus, or a square for each set of vertices. List all that apply.

11. $E(0, -3)$, $F(-3, 0)$, $G(0, 3)$, $H(3, 0)$ **parallelogram, rectangle, rhombus, square**

12. $E(2, 1)$, $F(3, 4)$, $G(7, 2)$, $H(6, -1)$ **parallelogram**

Practice

Trapezoids

MATH is an isosceles trapezoid with bases $\overline{MA}$ and $\overline{TH}$. Use the given information to solve each problem.

1. If $MA = 34$ and $HT = 20$, find CD.

2. If $HT = 17.6$ and $CD = 28.6$ find MA.

3. If $MA = 23.9$ and $CD = 16.4$, find HT.

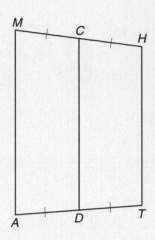

4. If $CD = x + 12$ and $MA + HT = 4x + 3$, find x.

5. If $m\angle TAM = 63$, find $m\angle HMA$.

6. If $m\angle HCD = 52$, find $m\angle TDC$.

7. If $m\angle DCM = 2x$, find $m\angle CMA$ in terms of x.

8. If the measure of the median of an isosceles trapezoid is 5.5, what are the possible integral measures for the bases?

9. $\overline{VW}$ is the median of a trapezoid that has bases $\overline{MN}$ and $\overline{PO}$, with V on $\overline{OM}$ and W on $\overline{PN}$. If the vertices of the trapezoid are $M(2, 6)$, $N(4, 6)$ $P(10, 0)$, and $O(0, 0)$, find the coordinates of V and W.

10. $\overline{VW}$ is the median of a trapezoid that has bases $\overline{MN}$ and $\overline{PO}$, with V on $\overline{PM}$ and W on $\overline{ON}$. If four of the points are $M(5, 10)$, $N(9, 10)$, $V(3, 7)$, and $W(11, 7)$, find the coordinates of P and O.

NAME_____ DATE _____

Practice

Trapezoids

MATH is an isosceles trapezoid with bases $\overline{MA}$ and $\overline{TH}$. Use the given information to solve each problem.

1. If $MA = 34$ and $HT = 20$, find CD. **27**

2. If $HT = 17.6$ and $CD = 28.6$ find MA. **39.6**

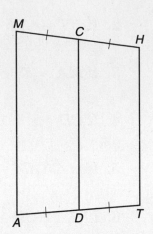

3. If $MA = 23.9$ and $CD = 16.4$, find HT. **8.9**

4. If $CD = x + 12$ and $MA + HT = 4x + 3$, find x. **10.5**

5. If $m\angle TAM = 63$, find $m\angle HMA$. **63**

6. If $m\angle HCD = 52$, find $m\angle TDC$. **52**

7. If $m\angle DCM = 2x$, find $m\angle CMA$ in terms of x. **$180 - 2x$**

8. If the measure of the median of an isosceles trapezoid is 5.5, what are the possible integral measures for the bases?
   1, 10; 2, 9; 3, 8; 4, 7; 5, 6

9. $\overline{VW}$ is the median of a trapezoid that has bases $\overline{MN}$ and $\overline{PO}$, with V on $\overline{OM}$ and W on $\overline{PN}$. If the vertices of the trapezoid are $M(2, 6)$, $N(4, 6)$ $P(10, 0)$, and $O(0, 0)$, find the coordinates of V and W. **$V(1, 3)$, $W(7, 3)$**

10. $\overline{VW}$ is the median of a trapezoid that has bases $\overline{MN}$ and $\overline{PO}$, with V on $\overline{PM}$ and W on $\overline{ON}$. If four of the points are $M(5, 10)$, $N(9, 10)$, $V(3, 7)$, and $W(11, 7)$, find the coordinates of P and O. **$P(1, 4)$, $O(13, 4)$**

NAME_____ DATE _____

Practice

Student Edition
Pages 338–345

Integration: Algebra
Using Proportions

Solve each proportion using cross products.

1. $\dfrac{3}{5} = \dfrac{x}{15}$

2. $\dfrac{20 - x}{x} = \dfrac{6}{4}$

3. $\dfrac{x + 1}{5} = \dfrac{x - 1}{2}$

4. $\dfrac{x}{x - 3} = \dfrac{x + 4}{x}$

5. $\dfrac{x + 1}{6} = \dfrac{x - 1}{x}$

6. $\dfrac{1}{x} = \dfrac{6}{x + 9}$

7. $\dfrac{x}{x + 8} = \dfrac{2}{3}$

8. $\dfrac{4}{12} = \dfrac{x + 2}{2x + 5}$

In the figure at the right, $\dfrac{AC}{CD} = \dfrac{CE}{CB}$. Use proportions to complete the table.

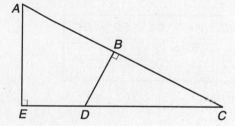

	AC	BC	AB	CE	ED	DC
9.	10	4		8		
10.	12			10		9

Use a proportion to solve each problem.

11. The ratio of seniors to juniors in the Math Club is 2:3. If there are 21 juniors, how many seniors are in the club?

12. A 15-foot building casts a 9-foot shadow. How tall is a building that casts a 30-foot shadow at the same time?

13. A photo that is 3 inches wide and 5 inches high was enlarged so that it is 12 inches wide. How high is the enlargement?

14. Philip has been eating 2 hamburgers every 5 days. At that rate, how many hamburgers will he eat in 30 days?

NAME _____ DATE _____

Practice

Integration: Algebra
Using Proportions

Solve each proportion using cross products.

1. $\frac{3}{5} = \frac{x}{15}$ **9**

2. $\frac{20-x}{x} = \frac{6}{4}$ **8**

3. $\frac{x+1}{5} = \frac{x-1}{2}$ **$\frac{7}{3}$**

4. $\frac{x}{x-3} = \frac{x+4}{x}$ **12**

5. $\frac{x+1}{6} = \frac{x-1}{x}$ **2, 3**

6. $\frac{1}{x} = \frac{6}{x+9}$ **$\frac{9}{5}$**

7. $\frac{x}{x+8} = \frac{2}{3}$ **16**

8. $\frac{4}{12} = \frac{x+2}{2x+5}$ **−1**

In the figure at the right, $\frac{AC}{CD} = \frac{CE}{CB}$. Use proportions to complete the table.

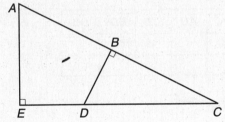

	AC	BC	AB	CE	ED	DC
9.	10	4	**6**	8	**3**	5
10.	12	7.5	**4.5**	10	**1**	9

Use a proportion to solve each problem.

11. The ratio of seniors to juniors in the Math Club is 2:3. If there are 21 juniors, how many seniors are in the club?
14 seniors

12. A 15-foot building casts a 9-foot shadow. How tall is a building that casts a 30-foot shadow at the same time? **50 ft**

13. A photo that is 3 inches wide and 5 inches high was enlarged so that it is 12 inches wide. How high is the enlargement?
20 in.

14. Philip has been eating 2 hamburgers every 5 days. At that rate, how many hamburgers will he eat in 30 days?
12 hamburgers

Exploring Similar Polygons

In the figure at the right, △ABC is similar to △DEF.

1. Write three equal ratios to show corresponding sides are proportional.

2. Find the value of x.

3. Find the value of y.

4. Find the ratio $\dfrac{m\angle A}{m\angle D}$.

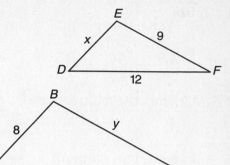

In the figure at the right, quadrilateral ABCD is similar to quadrilateral EFGH.

5. Write four equal ratios to show corresponding sides are proportional.

6. Find AB.

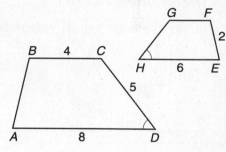

7. Find HG.

8. Find FG.

9. The sum of the measures of $\angle A$ and $\angle C$ equals the sum of the measures of which two angles of quadrilateral *EFGH*?

Practice

Exploring Similar Polygons

In the figure at the right, △ABC is similar to △DEF.

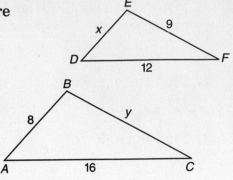

1. Write three equal ratios to show corresponding sides are proportional.
$$\frac{AB}{DE} = \frac{AC}{DF} = \frac{BC}{EF}$$

2. Find the value of x. **6**

3. Find the value of y. **12**

4. Find the ratio $\frac{m\angle A}{m\angle D}$. $\frac{1}{1}$

In the figure at the right, quadrilateral ABCD is similar to quadrilateral EFGH.

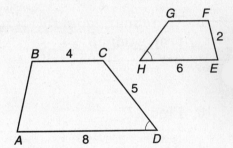

5. Write four equal ratios to show corresponding sides are proportional. $\frac{AB}{EF} = \frac{BC}{FG} = \frac{CD}{GH} = \frac{DA}{HE}$

6. Find AB. $2\frac{2}{3}$

7. Find HG. $3\frac{3}{4}$

8. Find FG. **3**

9. The sum of the measures of $\angle A$ and $\angle C$ equals the sum of the measures of which two angles of quadrilateral *EFGH*?
$\angle E$ and $\angle G$

Practice

Identifying Similar Triangles

Identify the similar triangles in each figure. Explain why they are similar and use the given information to find x and y.

1.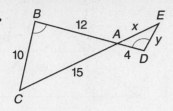

2.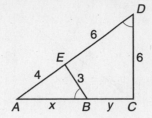

3.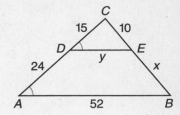

Write a two-column proof.

4. Given: $\overline{AB} \parallel \overline{EF}$
$\overline{AC} \parallel \overline{DF}$

Prove: $\triangle ABC \sim \triangle FED$

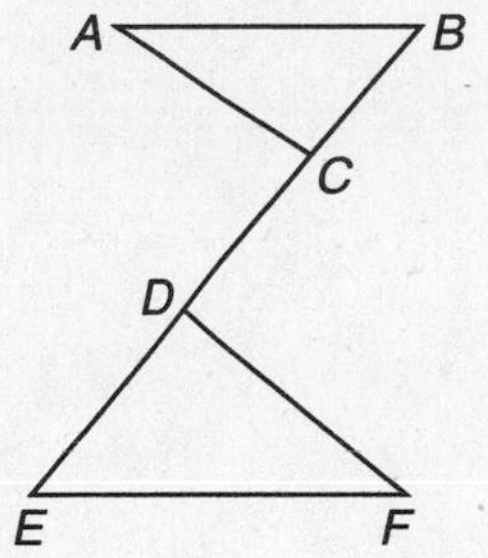

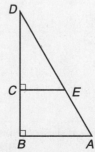

Proof:

Statements	Reasons

5. Given: $\overline{AB} \perp \overline{BD}$
$\overline{ED} \perp \overline{BD}$

Prove: $\triangle BDA \sim \triangle CDE$

Proof:

Statements	Reasons

Identifying Similar Triangles

Identify the similar triangles in each figure. Explain why they are similar and use the given information to find x and y.

1.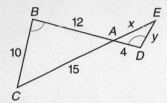

$\triangle ABC \sim \triangle ADE$;

AA; 5, $3\frac{1}{3}$

2.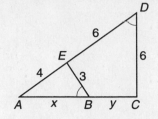

$\triangle ABE \sim \triangle ADC$;

AA; 5, 3

3.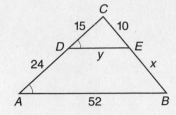

$\triangle ABC \sim \triangle DEC$;

AA; 16, 20

Write a two-column proof.

4. Given: $\overline{AB} \parallel \overline{EF}$
   $\overline{AC} \parallel \overline{DF}$
   Prove: $\triangle ABC \sim \triangle FED$

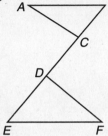

Proof:

Statements	Reasons
a. $\overline{AB} \parallel \overline{EF}$	a. Given
b. $\angle B \cong \angle E$	b. If two $\parallel$ lines are cut by a transversal, alt. int. $\angle$s are $\cong$.
c. $\overline{AC} \parallel \overline{DF}$	c. Given
d. $\angle ACB \cong \angle FDE$	d. If two $\parallel$ lines are cut by a transversal, alt. ext. $\angle$s are $\cong$.
e. $\triangle ABC \sim \triangle FED$	e. AA Similarity

5. Given: $\overline{AB} \perp \overline{BD}$
   $\overline{ED} \perp \overline{BD}$
   Prove: $\triangle BDA \sim \triangle CDE$

Proof:

Statements	Reasons
a. $\overline{AB} \perp \overline{BD}$ $\overline{EC} \perp \overline{BD}$	a. Given
b. $\angle ABD, \angle ECD$ are rt. $\angle$s.	b. $\perp$ lines form four rt. $\angle$s.
c. $\angle ABD \cong \angle ECD$	c. All rt. $\angle$s are $\cong$.
d. $\angle D \cong \angle D$	d. Congruence of $\angle$s is reflexive.
e. $\triangle BDA \sim \triangle CDE$	e. AA Similarity

NAME_____ DATE _____

Practice

Parallel Lines and Proportional Parts

Refer to the figure at the right for Exercises 1–2. Determine whether it is always true that $\overline{AB} \parallel \overline{YZ}$ under the given conditions.

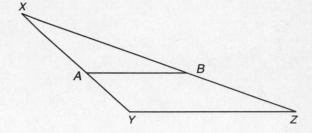

1. $XA = 6$
   $AY = 4$
   $XB = 8$
   $BZ = 5$

2. $XB = 3$
   $BZ = 2$
   $AB = 6$
   $YZ = 10$

In $\triangle PQR$, find x and y so that $\overline{JG} \parallel \overline{RQ}$.

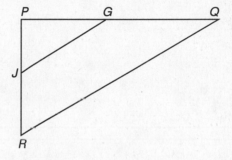

3. $PJ = 6$
   $JG = 5$
   $PG = 4$
   $GQ = x$
   $RQ = x + 6$
   $JR = y$

4. $RQ = 10$
   $JG = 8$
   $PJ = 8x - 5$
   $JR = x$
   $PG = 3y + 2$
   $QG = y$

5. In the figure at the right, $\overrightarrow{YA} \parallel \overrightarrow{OE} \parallel \overrightarrow{BR}$.
   Find the values of x and y if $YO = 4$,
   $ER = 16$, and $AR = 24$.

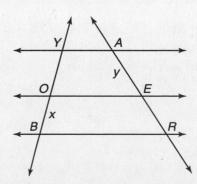

           Geometry

Practice

Parallel Lines and Proportional Parts

Refer to the figure at the right for Exercises 1–2. Determine whether it is always true that $\overline{AB} \parallel \overline{YZ}$ under the given conditions.

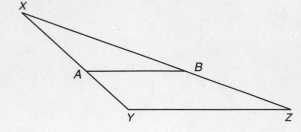

1. $XA = 6$
$AY = 4$
$XB = 8$
$BZ = 5$ **no**

2. $XB = 3$
$BZ = 2$
$AB = 6$
$YZ = 10$ **no**

In $\triangle PQR$, find x and y so that $\overline{JG} \parallel \overline{RQ}$.

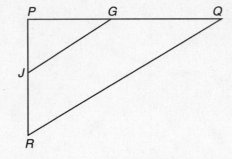

3. $PJ = 6$
$JG = 5$
$PG = 4$
$GQ = x$
$RQ = x + 6$
$JR = y$ **4, 6**

4. $RQ = 10$
$JG = 8$
$PJ = 8x - 5$
$JR = x$
$PG = 3y + 2$
$QG = y$ $\frac{5}{4}$, **2**

5. In the figure at the right, $\overleftrightarrow{YA} \parallel \overleftrightarrow{OE} \parallel \overleftrightarrow{BR}$. Find the values of x and y if $YO = 4$, $ER = 16$, and $AR = 24$. **8, 8**

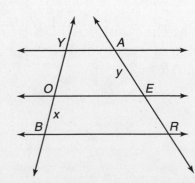

Practice

Parts of Similar Triangles

In the figure at the right, △ABC ~ △DEF, $\overline{BR} \cong \overline{RC}$, and $\overline{ES} \cong \overline{SF}$. Find the value of x.

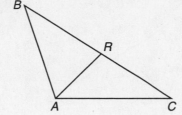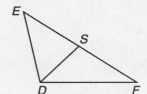

1. $BC = 24$
   $EF = 15$
   $AR = x$
   $DS = x - 6$

2. $AB = 2x + 5$
   $DE = x + 7$
   $AR = 24$
   $DS = 18$

Find the value of x.

3.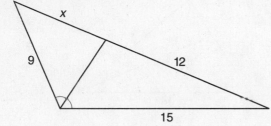

4.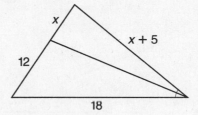

In the figure at the right, △ABC ~ △DEF, and $\overline{BX}$ and $\overline{EY}$ are altitudes. Find the value of x.

5. $AB = 25$
   $DE = 16$
   $BX = 18$
   $EY = x$

6. $AB = 30$
   $DE = 25$
   $BX = 2x + 5$
   $EY = x + 10$

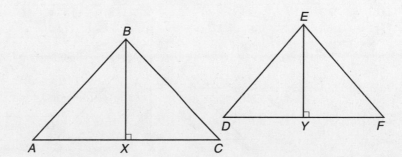

7–5

NAME______________________________ DATE ____________

Practice

Student Edition
Pages 370–377

Parts of Similar Triangles

In the figure at the right, $\triangle ABC \sim \triangle DEF$, $\overline{BR} \cong \overline{RC}$, and $\overline{ES} \cong \overline{SF}$. Find the value of x.

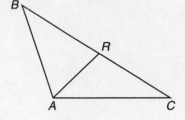

1. $BC = 24$
$EF = 15$
$AR = x$
$DS = x - 6$ **16**

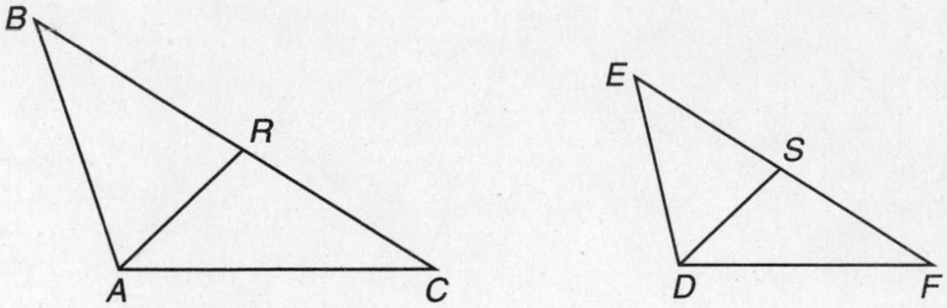

2. $AB = 2x + 5$
$DE = x + 7$
$AR = 24$
$DS = 18$ **6.5**

Find the value of x.

3.

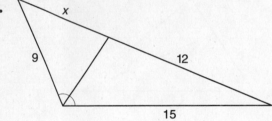

7.2

4.

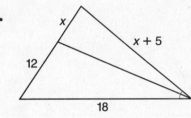

10

In the figure at the right, $\triangle ABC \sim \triangle DEF$, and $\overline{BX}$ and $\overline{EY}$ are altitudes. Find the value of x.

5. $AB = 25$
$DE = 16$
$BX = 18$
$EY = x$ **11.52**

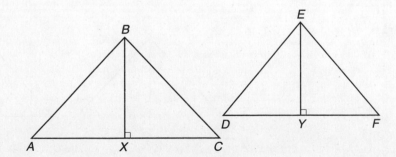

6. $AB = 30$
$DE = 25$
$BX = 2x + 5$
$EY = x + 10$ **8.75**

Fractals and Self-Similarity

Use the drawings below of three stages of a variation on the Koch curve to complete Exercises 1 and 2.

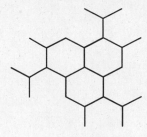

Stage 1   Stage 2   Stage 3

1. Draw Stage 4.

2. Describe the iterative process used in this variation.

3. Draw an equilateral triangle. Divide each side into fourths, and connect the points to form three lines parallel to each side of the triangle.

4. Find the number of similar triangles within the figure in Exercise 3.

5. Create a figure and draw stages 1–3 of iteration.

6. Describe the iterative process used in Exercise 5.

7. Solve a Simpler Problem How many diagonals can be drawn for a polygon with 15 sides?

Practice

Fractals and Self-Similarity

Use the drawings below of three stages of a variation on the Koch curve to complete Exercises 1 and 2.

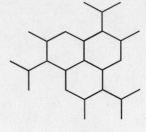

Stage 1   Stage 2   Stage 3

1. Draw Stage 4.

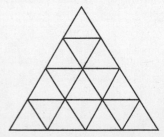

2. Describe the iterative process used in this variation. **Two similar branches are drawn at the end of one segment of the previous branch.**

3. Draw an equilateral triangle. Divide each side into fourths, and connect the points to form three lines parallel to each side of the triangle.

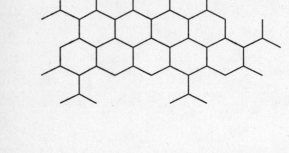

4. Find the number of similar triangles within the figure in Exercise 3. **27**

5. Create a figure and draw stages 1–3 of iteration. **See student's work.**

6. Describe the iterative process used in Exercise 5. **See student's work.**

7. Solve a Simpler Problem How many diagonals can be drawn for a polygon with 15 sides? **90**

Geometric Mean and the Pythagorean Theorem

Find the geometric mean between each pair of numbers.

1. 5 and 10

2. 3 and 27

3. 6 and $\frac{1}{2}$

4. 16 and $\frac{1}{9}$

Find the values of x and y.

5.

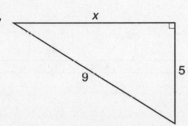

6.

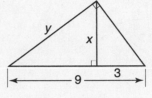

7.

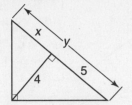

8.

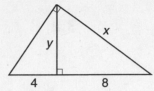

9.

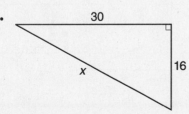

10.

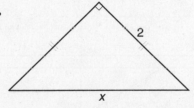

11.

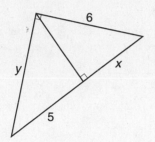

12.

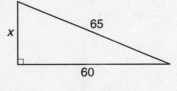

Determine if the given measures are measures of the sides of a right triangle.

13. 14, 48, 50

14. 50, 75, 85

15. 15, 36, 39

16. 45, 60, 80

Practice

Geometric Mean and the Pythagorean Theorem

Find the geometric mean between each pair of numbers.

1. 5 and 10 $5\sqrt{2} \approx 7.1$

2. 3 and 27 **9**

3. 6 and $\frac{1}{2}$ $\sqrt{3} \approx 1.7$

4. 16 and $\frac{1}{9}$ $\frac{4}{3}$

Find the values of x and y.

5. 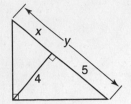 **3.2, 8.2**

6. 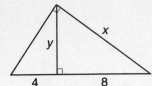 $4\sqrt{6} \approx 9.8,$ $4\sqrt{2} \approx 5.7$

7. 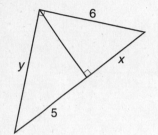 $4, 3\sqrt{5} \approx 6.7$

8. 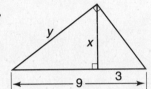 $3\sqrt{2} \approx 4.2,$ $3\sqrt{6} \approx 7.3$

9.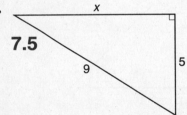

10. **2.8**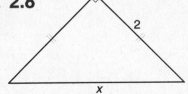

11.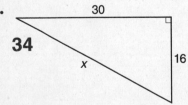

12. 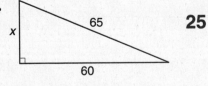 **25**

Determine if the given measures are measures of the sides of a right triangle.

13. 14, 48, 50 **yes**

14. 50, 75, 85 **no**

15. 15, 36, 39 **yes**

16. 45, 60, 80 **no**

NAME_____ DATE _____

Practice

Special Right Triangles

Find the values of x and y.

1.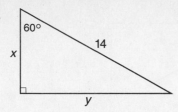

2.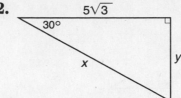

3.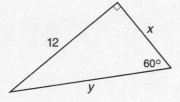

4.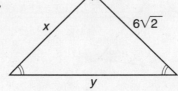

5.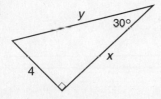

6.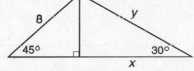

7. Find the length of a diagonal of a square with sides 10 in. long.

8. Find the length of a side of a square whose diagonal is 4 cm.

9. One side of an equilateral triangle measures 6 cm. Find the measure of an altitude of the triangle.

44

Practice

Special Right Triangles

Find the values of x and y.

1.

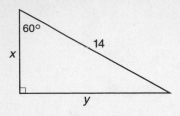

7, 7√3 ≈ 12.1

2.

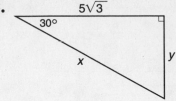

10, 5

3.

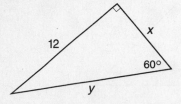

4√3 ≈ 6.9,
8√3 ≈ 13.8

4.

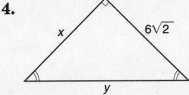

6√2 ≈ 8.5, 12

5.

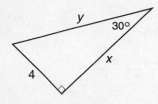

4√3 ≈ 6.9, 8

6.

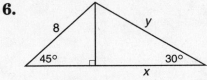

4√6 ≈ 9.8,
8√2 ≈ 11.3

7. Find the length of a diagonal of a square with sides 10 in. long.
10√2 ≈ 14.1 in.

8. Find the length of a side of a square whose diagonal is 4 cm.
2√2 ≈ 2.8 cm

9. One side of an equilateral triangle measures 6 cm. Find the measure of an altitude of the triangle. **3√3 ≈ 5.2 cm**

NAME_____ DATE_____

Practice

Student Edition
Pages 412–419

Integration: Trigonometry
Ratios in Right Triangles

Find the values of x and y. Round to the nearest tenth.

1.
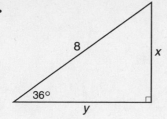

2.
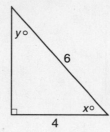

3.
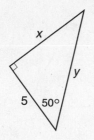

4.
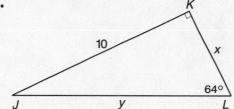

5.
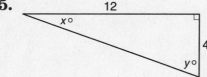

6.
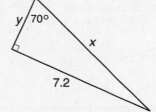

Geometry

Practice

Integration: Trigonometry
Ratios in Right Triangles

Find the values of x and y. Round to the nearest tenth.

1.

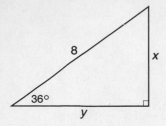

$x \approx 4.7, y \approx 6.5$

2.

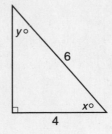

$x \approx 48.2, y \approx 41.8$

3.

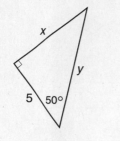

$x \approx 6.0, y \approx 7.8$

4.

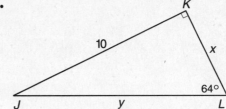

$x \approx 4.9, y \approx 11.1$

5.

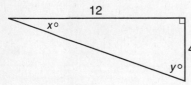

$x \approx 18.4, y \approx 71.6$

6.

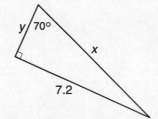

$x \approx 7.7, y \approx 2.6$

NAME_____ DATE _____

Practice

Angles of Elevation and Depression

Solve each problem. Round measures of segments to the nearest hundredth and measures of angles to the nearest degree.

1. A 20-foot ladder leans against a wall so that the base of the ladder is 8 feet from the base of the building. What angle does the ladder make with the ground?

2. A 50-meter vertical tower is braced with a cable secured at the top of the tower and tied 30 meters from the base. What angles does the cable form with the vertical tower?

3. At a point on the ground 50 feet from the foot of a tree, the angle of elevation to the top of the tree is 53°. Find the height of the tree.

4. From the top of a lighthouse 210 feet high, the angle of depression of a boat is 27°. Find the distance from the boat to the food of the lighthouse. The lighthouse was built at sea level.

5. Richard is flying a kite. The kite string makes an angle of 57° with the ground. If Richard is standing 100 feet from the point on the ground directly below the kite, find the length of the kite string.

6. An airplane rises vertically 1000 feet over a horizontal distance of 1 mile. What is the angle of elevation of the airplane's path?

Geometry

Practice

Angles of Elevation and Depression

Solve each problem. Round measures of segments to the nearest hundredth and measures of angles to the nearest degree.

1. A 20-foot ladder leans against a wall so that the base of the ladder is 8 feet from the base of the building. What angle does the ladder make with the ground? **66°**

2. A 50-meter vertical tower is braced with a cable secured at the top of the tower and tied 30 meters from the base. What angles does the cable form with the vertical tower? **31°**

3. At a point on the ground 50 feet from the foot of a tree, the angle of elevation to the top of the tree is 53°. Find the height of the tree. **66.35 ft**

4. From the top of a lighthouse 210 feet high, the angle of depression of a boat is 27°. Find the distance from the boat to the food of the lighthouse. The lighthouse was built at sea level. **412.15 ft**

5. Richard is flying a kite. The kite string makes an angle of 57° with the ground. If Richard is standing 100 feet from the point on the ground directly below the kite, find the length of the kite string. **183.61 ft**

6. An airplane rises vertically 1000 feet over a horizontal distance of 1 mile. What is the angle of elevation of the airplane's path? **11°**

Using the Law of Sines

Solve each △ ABC. Round measures to the nearest tenth.

1. $a = 12, m\angle B = 70, m\angle C = 15$

2. $a = 12, b = 5, m\angle A = 110$

3. $a = 8, m\angle A = 60, m\angle C = 40$

4. $a = 5, c = 4, m\angle A = 65$

5. $b = 6, m\angle A = 44, m\angle B = 68$

6. $a = 7, m\angle A = 37, m\angle B = 76$

7. $a = 9, b = 9, m\angle C = 20°$

8. A ship is sighted from two radar stations 43 km apart. The angle between the line segment joining the two stations and the radar beam of the first station is 37°. The angle between the line segment joining the two stations and the beam from the second station is 113°. How far is the ship from the second station?

Using the Law of Sines

Solve each △ABC. Round measures to the nearest tenth.

1. $a = 12$, $m\angle B = 70$, $m\angle C = 15$ **$m\angle A = 95$, $b \approx 11.3$, $c \approx 3.1$**

2. $a = 12$, $b = 5$, $m\angle A = 110$ **$m\angle B \approx 23.1$, $m\angle C \approx 46.9$, $c \approx 9.3$**

3. $a = 8$, $m\angle A = 60$, $m\angle C = 40$ **$m\angle B = 80$, $b \approx 9.1$, $c \approx 5.9$**

4. $a = 5$, $c = 4$, $m\angle A = 65$ **$m\angle C \approx 46.5$, $m\angle B \approx 68.5$, $b \approx 5.2$**

5. $b = 6$, $m\angle A = 44$, $m\angle B = 68$ **$m\angle C = 68$, $a \approx 4.5$, $c = 6$**

6. $a = 7$, $m\angle A = 37$, $m\angle B = 76$ **$m\angle C = 67$, $b \approx 11.3$, $c \approx 10.7$**

7. $a = 9$, $b = 9$, $m\angle C = 20°$ **$m\angle A = 80$, $m\angle B = 80$, $c \approx 3.1$**

8. A ship is sighted from two radar stations 43 km apart. The angle between the line segment joining the two stations and the radar beam of the first station is 37°. The angle between the line segment joining the two stations and the beam from the second station is 113°. How far is the ship from the second station? **51.8 km**

NAME ______________________ DATE __________

Practice

Student Edition
Pages 431–436

Using the Law of Cosines

Solve each triangle △ABC described below. Round measures to the nearest tenth.

1. $a = 16, b = 20, m\angle B = 40$

2. $a = 10, b = 15, c = 12$

3. $a = 42, c = 60, m\angle B = 58$

4. $m\angle A = 60, m\angle B = 72, c = 9$

5. $a = 7, b = 12, c = 15$

6. $m\angle A = 43, b = 23, c = 26$

7. $a = 16, m\angle A = 23, m\angle B = 87$

8. $c = 15.6, a = 12.9, b = 18.4$

9. Decision-Making Complete the addition problem at the right. If a letter is used more than once, it represents the same digit each time.

```
  SOME
 +MORE
 -----
 SENSE
```

NAME _____ DATE _____

Practice

Using the Law of Cosines

Solve each triangle △ABC described below. Round measures to the nearest tenth.

1. $a = 16, b = 20, m\angle B = 40$

$m\angle A \approx 30.9$

$m\angle C \approx 109.1$

$c \approx 29.4$

2. $a = 10, b = 15, c = 12$

$m\angle A \approx 41.6$

$m\angle B \approx 84.8$

$m\angle C \approx 53.6$

3. $a = 42, c = 60, m\angle B = 58$

$m\angle A \approx 43.3$

$m\angle C \approx 78.7$

$b \approx 51.9$

4. $m\angle A = 60, m\angle B = 72, c = 9$

$m\angle C \approx 48$

$a \approx 10.5$

$b \approx 11.5$

5. $a = 7, b = 12, c = 15$

$m\angle A \approx 26.6$

$m\angle B \approx 50.1$

$m\angle C \approx 103.3$

6. $m\angle A = 43, b = 23, c = 26$

$m\angle B \approx 59.5$

$m\angle C \approx 77.5$

$a \approx 18.2$

7. $a = 16, m\angle A = 23, m\angle B = 87$

$m\angle C \approx 70$

$b \approx 40.9$

$c \approx 38.5$

8. $c = 15.6, a = 12.9, b = 18.4$

$m\angle A \approx 43.6$

$m\angle B \approx 79.6$

$m\angle C \approx 56.8$

9. Decision-Making Complete the addition problem at the right. If a letter is used more than once, it represents the same digit each time.

$$\begin{array}{r} \text{SOME} \\ +\text{MORE} \\ \hline \text{SENSE} \end{array} \quad \begin{array}{r} 1780 \\ +8730 \\ \hline 10510 \end{array}$$

Geometry

Exploring Circles

Refer to the figure at the right.

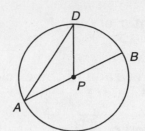

1. Name the center of ⊙*P*.

2. Name the three radii of the circle.

3. Name a diameter.

4. Name two chords.

Find the circumference of a circle with a radius of the given length. Round your answers to the nearest tenth.

5. 3 cm

6. 2 ft

7. 34 mm

8. 4.5 m

Find the exact circumference of each circle.

9.

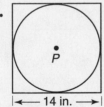

← 14 in. →

10.

10 cm

24 cm

11.

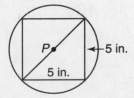

←5 in.

5 in.

12.

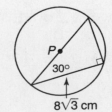

30°

8√3 cm

NAME _____ DATE _____

Practice

Exploring Circles

Refer to the figure at the right.

1. Name the center of ⊙P. **P**

2. Name the three radii of the circle.
   PA, PD, PB

3. Name a diameter. **$\overline{AB}$**

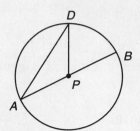

4. Name two chords. **$\overline{AD}, \overline{AB}$**

Find the circumference of a circle with a radius of the given length. Round your answers to the nearest tenth.

5. 3 cm **18.8 cm**

6. 2 ft **12.6 ft**

7. 34 mm **213.6 mm**

8. 4.5 m **28.3 m**

Find the exact circumference of each circle.

9. 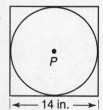 **14π in.**

10. 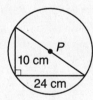 **26π cm**

11. 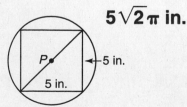 **5√2 π in.**

12. 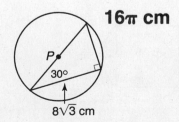 **16π cm**

Angles and Arcs

In ⊙P, m∠1 = 140 with diameter $\overline{AC}$. Find each measure.

1. $m\angle 2$

2. $m\widehat{BC}$

3. $m\widehat{AB}$

4. $m\widehat{ABC}$

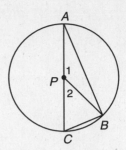

In ⊙P, m∠2 = m∠1, m∠2 = 4x + 35, m∠1 = 9x + 5 with diameters $\overline{BD}$ and $\overline{AC}$. Find each of the following.

5. x

6. $m\widehat{AE}$

7. $m\widehat{ED}$

8. $m\angle 3$

9. $m\widehat{AB}$

10. $m\widehat{EC}$

11. $m\widehat{EB}$

12. $m\angle CPB$

13. $m\widehat{CB}$

14. $m\widehat{CEB}$

15. $m\widehat{DC}$

16. $m\widehat{CEA}$

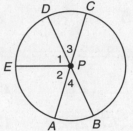

17. In ⊙A, $AB = 12$ and $m\angle BAC = 60$.
    Find the length of $\widehat{BC}$.

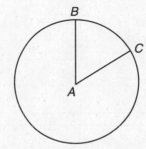

18. **Using Graphs** The table below
    shows how federal funds were spent
    on education in 1990.

1990 Federal Funds Spent for Education	
Elementary/Secondary	$ 7,945,177
Education for the Disabled	4,204,099
Post-Secondary Education	12,645,630
Public Library Services	145,367
Other	760,616
Total	$25,700,889

a. Use the information to make a circle graph.

b. Out of the $12,645,630 spent on post-secondary education,
   $10,801,185 went to post-secondary financial assistance. What
   percent is that of the $12,645,630?

Angles and Arcs

In ⊙P, m∠1 = 140 with diameter $\overline{AC}$. Find each measure.

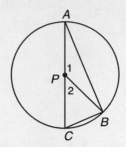

1. $m\angle 2$ **40**   2. $m\widehat{BC}$ **40**

3. $m\widehat{AB}$ **140**   4. $m\widehat{ABC}$ **180**

In ⊙P, m∠2 = m∠1, m∠2 = 4x + 35, m∠1 = 9x + 5 with diameters $\overline{BD}$ and $\overline{AC}$. Find each of the following.

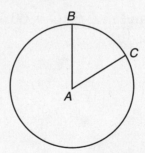

5. x **6**   6. $m\widehat{AE}$ **59**   7. $m\widehat{ED}$ **59**

8. $m\angle 3$ **62**   9. $m\widehat{AB}$ **62**   10. $m\widehat{EC}$ **121**

11. $m\widehat{EB}$ **121**   12. $m\angle CPB$ **118**   13. $m\widehat{CB}$ **118**

14. $m\widehat{CEB}$ **242**   15. $m\widehat{DC}$ **62**   16. $m\widehat{CEA}$ **180**

17. In ⊙A, $AB = 12$ and $m\angle BAC = 60$. Find the length of $\widehat{BC}$. **12.6**

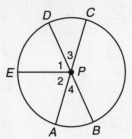

18. **Using Graphs**   The table below shows how federal funds were spent on education in 1990.

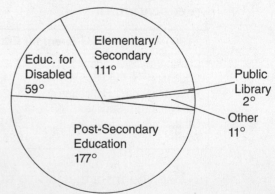

1990 Federal Funds Spent for Education

1990 Federal Funds Spent for Education	
Elementary/Secondary	$ 7,945,177
Education for the Disabled	4,204,099
Post-Secondary Education	12,645,630
Public Library Services	145,367
Other	760,616
Total	$25,700,889

a. Use the information to make a circle graph.

b. Out of the $12,645,630 spent on post-secondary education, $10,801,185 went to post-secondary financial assistance. What percent is that of the $12,645,630? **85.4%**

NAME _____ DATE _____

Practice

Student Edition
Pages 459–465

Arcs and Chords

In each figure, O is the center. Find each measure to the nearest tenth.

1. $m\overarc{BC}$

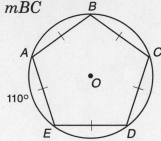

2. YQ

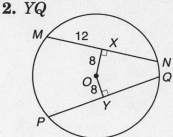

3. Suppose a chord of a circle is 16 inches long and is 6 inches from the center of the circle. Find the length of a radius.

4. Find the length of a chord that is 5 inches from the center of a circle with a radius of 13 inches.

5. Suppose a radius of a circle is 17 units and a chord is 30 units long. Find the distance from the center of the circle to the chord.

6. Find AB.

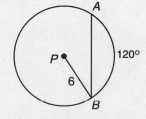

7. Find AB

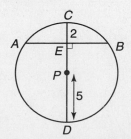

Geometry

NAME_____ DATE _____

Practice

Student Edition
Pages 459–465

Arcs and Chords

In each figure, O is the center. Find each measure to the nearest tenth.

1. $m\widehat{BC}$

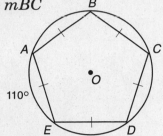

62.5

2. YQ

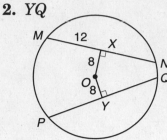

12

3. Suppose a chord of a circle is 16 inches long and is 6 inches from the center of the circle. Find the length of a radius. **10 in.**

4. Find the length of a chord that is 5 inches from the center of a circle with a radius of 13 inches. **24 in.**

5. Suppose a radius of a circle is 17 units and a chord is 30 units long. Find the distance from the center of the circle to the chord. **8 units**

6. Find AB.

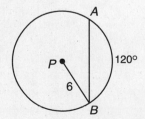

$6\sqrt{3}$ or about 10.4

7. Find AB

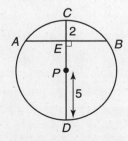

8

Practice

Inscribed Angles

In ⊙P, m$\widehat{AB}$ = x and m$\widehat{BC}$ = 3x. Find each measure.

1. m$\widehat{ADC}$

2. m$\widehat{AB}$

3. m$\widehat{BC}$

4. m∠ABC

5. m∠A

6. m∠C

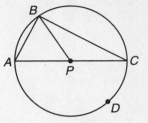

In ⊙Q, m∠ABC = 72 and m$\widehat{CD}$ = 46. Find each measure.

7. m$\widehat{CA}$

8. m$\widehat{AD}$

9. m∠ABD

10. m$\widehat{BC}$

11. m∠C

12. m∠A

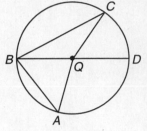

13. Suppose ABCD is a trapezoid that has its vertices on ⊙P, with AB ∥ CD. Write a paragraph proof to show that ABCD is an isosceles trapezoid.

Inscribed Angles

In ⊙P, m$\widehat{AB}$ = x and m$\widehat{BC}$ = 3x. Find each measure.

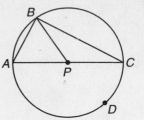

1. m$\widehat{ADC}$ **180**

4. m∠ABC **90**

2. m$\widehat{AB}$ **45**

5. m∠A **67.5**

3. m$\widehat{BC}$ **135**

6. m∠C **22.5**

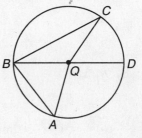

In ⊙Q, m∠ABC = 72 and m$\widehat{CD}$ = 46. Find each measure.

7. m$\widehat{CA}$ **144**

10. m$\widehat{BC}$ **134**

8. m$\widehat{AD}$ **98**

11. m∠C **23**

9. m∠ABD **49**

12. m∠A **49**

13. Suppose ABCD is a trapezoid that has its vertices on ⊙P, with AB ∥ CD. Write a paragraph proof to show that ABCD is an isosceles trapezoid.
∠A and ∠D are supplementary, since they are consecutive interior angles formed by two parallel lines and a transversal. ∠B and ∠D are supplementary, since they are opposite angles of a quadrilateral inscribed in a circle. It follows that $\widehat{ADC}$ ≅ $\widehat{DCB}$. By the arc addition postulate and the subtraction property of equality, m$\widehat{AD}$ = m$\widehat{BC}$. Thus $\widehat{AD}$ ≅ $\widehat{BC}$ and, since if two arcs in a circle are congruent then their chords are congruent, AD ≅ BC. Trapezoid ABCD is isosceles by definition.

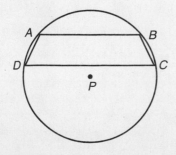

NAME_____ DATE _____

Practice

Tangents

For each ⊙Q, find the value of x. Assume that segments that appear to be tangent are tangent.

1.

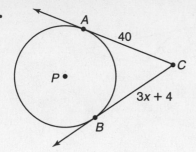

2.

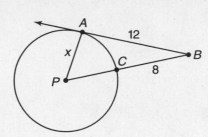

3.

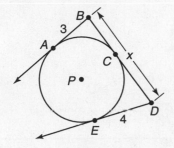

4.

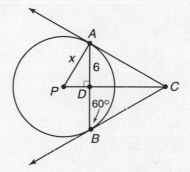

5.

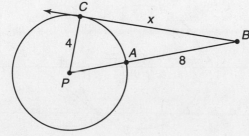

6.

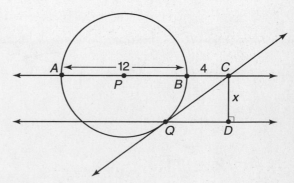

Tangents

For each ⊙Q, find the value of x. Assume that segments that appear to be tangent are tangent.

1.

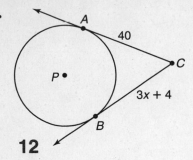

12

2.

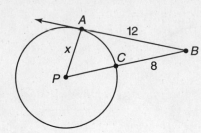

5

3.

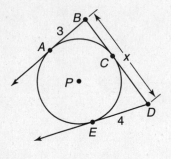

7

4.

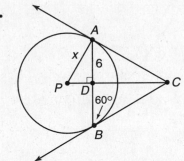

$4\sqrt{3} \approx 6.9$

5.

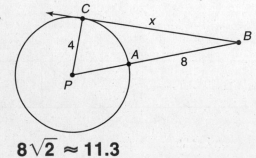

$8\sqrt{2} \approx 11.3$

6.

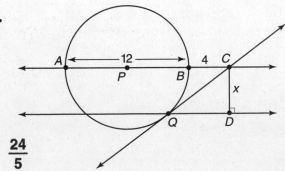

$\dfrac{24}{5}$

NAME_____ DATE _____

Student Edition
Pages 483–490

Practice

Secants, Tangents, and Angle Measures

Assume that lines that appear to be tangents are tangents.

In ⊙Q, m∠CQD = 120, mBC = 30, and m∠BEC = 25.
Find each measure.

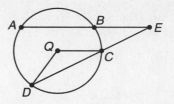

1. $m\widehat{DC}$ 2. $m\widehat{AD}$

3. $m\widehat{AB}$ 4. $m\angle QDC$

In ⊙Q, mAE = 140, mBD = y, mAB = 2y, and mDE = 2y.
Find each measure.

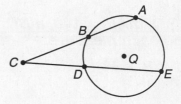

5. $m\widehat{BD}$ 6. $m\widehat{AB}$

7. $m\widehat{DE}$ 8. $m\angle BCD$

In ⊙P, mBC = 4x − 50, mDE = x + 25, mEF = x − 15,
mCD = x, and mFB = 50. Find each measure.

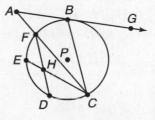

9. $m\angle A$ 10. $m\angle BCA$

11. $m\angle ABC$ 12. $m\angle GBC$

13. $m\angle FHE$ 14. $m\angle CFD$

In ⊙P, m∠A = 62 and mBD = 120. Find each measure.

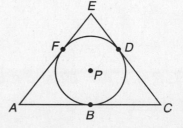

15. $m\angle C$ 16. $m\widehat{DF}$

17. $m\angle E$

9-6

Practice

Secants, Tangents, and Angle Measures

Assume that lines that appear to be tangents are tangents.

In ⊙Q, m∠CQD = 120, m$\widehat{BC}$ = 30, and m∠BEC = 25.
Find each measure.

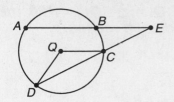

1. m$\widehat{DC}$ **120**

2. m$\widehat{AD}$ **80**

3. m$\widehat{AB}$ **130**

4. m∠QDC **30**

In ⊙Q, m$\widehat{AE}$ = 140, m$\widehat{BD}$ = y, m$\widehat{AB}$ = 2y, and m$\widehat{DE}$ = 2y.
Find each measure.

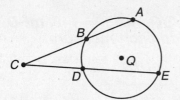

5. m$\widehat{BD}$ **44**

6. m$\widehat{AB}$ **88**

7. m$\widehat{DE}$ **88**

8. m∠BCD **48**

In ⊙P, m$\widehat{BC}$ = 4x − 50, m$\widehat{DE}$ = x + 25, m$\widehat{EF}$ = x − 15,
m$\widehat{CD}$ = x, and m$\widehat{FB}$ = 50. Find each measure.

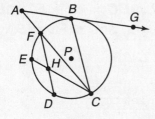

9. m∠A **50**

10. m∠BCA **25**

11. m∠ABC **105**

12. m∠GBC **75**

13. m∠FHE **42.5**

14. m∠CFD **25**

In ⊙P, m∠A = 62 and m$\widehat{BD}$ = 120. Find each measure.

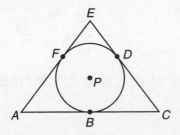

15. m∠C **60**

16. m$\widehat{DF}$ **122**

17. m∠E **58**

Special Segments in a Circle

Find the value of x to the nearest tenth. Assume segments that appear to be tangents are tangents.

1.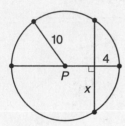

2.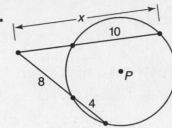

3.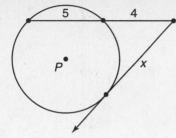

4.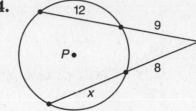

In ⊙P, CE = 6, CD = 16, and AB = 17. Find each measure.

5. EB

6. AE

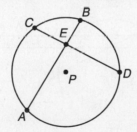

In ⊙P, AC = 3, BC = 5, and AD = 2. Find each measure.

7. PD

8. ED

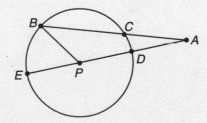

9. PB

NAME _____ DATE _____

Practice

Special Segments in a Circle

Find the value of x to the nearest tenth. Assume segments that appear to be tangents are tangents.

1.

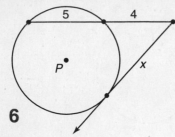

6

2.

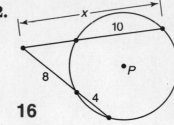

16

3.

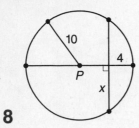

8

4.

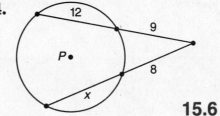

15.6

In ⊙P, CE = 6, CD = 16, and AB = 17. Find each measure.

5. *EB* **5**

6. *AE* **12**

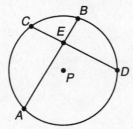

In ⊙P, AC = 3, BC = 5, and AD = 2. Find each measure.

7. *PD* **5**

8. *ED* **10**

9. *PB* **5**

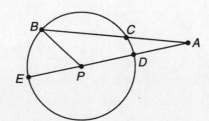

Geometry

Integration: Algebra
Equations of Circles

Determine the coordinates of the center and the measure of the radius for each circle whose equation is given.

1. $(x - 3)^2 + (y + 1)^2 = 16$

2. $\left(x + \dfrac{5}{8}\right)^2 + (y + 2)^2 - \dfrac{25}{7} = 0$

3. $(x - 3.2)^2 + (y - 0.75)^2 = 37.21$

Graph each circle whose equation is given. Label the center and measure of the radius on each graph.

4. $(x - 2)^2 + y^2 = 6.25$

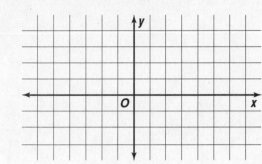

5. $(x + 3)^2 + \left(y - \dfrac{3}{2}\right)^2 = 4$

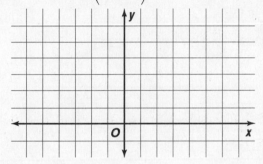

Write the equation of circle P based on the given information.

7. center: $P\left(0, \dfrac{1}{2}\right)$
   radius: 8

8. center: $P(-5.3, 1)$
   diameter: 9

9.

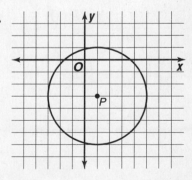

10. Write the equation of the circle that has a diameter whose endpoints are $(5, -7)$ and $(-2, 4)$.

NAME_____ DATE _____

Practice

Integration: Algebra
Equations of Circles

Determine the coordinates of the center and the measure of the radius for each circle whose equation is given.

1. $(x - 3)^2 + (y + 1)^2 = 16$

   (3, –1), r = 4

2. $\left(x + \dfrac{5}{8}\right)^2 + (y + 2)^2 - \dfrac{25}{7} = 0$

   $\left(-\dfrac{5}{8}, -2\right), r = \dfrac{5}{3}$

3. $(x - 3.2)^2 + (y - 0.75)^2 = 37.21$
   (3.2, 0.75), r = 6.1

Graph each circle whose equation is given. Label the center and measure of the radius on each graph.

4. $(x - 2)^2 + y^2 = 6.25$

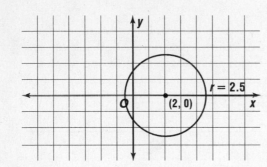

5. $(x + 3)^2 + \left(y - \dfrac{3}{2}\right)^2 = 4$

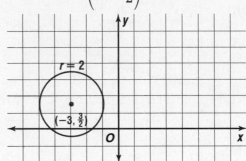

Write the equation of circle P based on the given information.

7. center: $P\left(0, \dfrac{1}{2}\right)$
   radius: 8

   $x^2 + \left(y - \dfrac{1}{2}\right)^2 = 64$

8. center: $P(-5.3, 1)$
   diameter: 9

   $(x + 5.3)^2 + (y - 1)^2 = 20.25$

9.

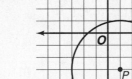

   $(x - 1)^2 + (y + 3)^2 = 16$

10. Write the equation of the circle that has a diameter whose endpoints are (5, –7) and (–2, 4).

   $\left(x - \dfrac{3}{2}\right)^2 + \left(y + \dfrac{3}{2}\right)^2 = 42.25$

NAME_____ DATE _____

Practice

Polygons

State the number of sides for each convex polygon.

1. quadrilateral

2. octagon

3. 83-gon

4. heptagon

5. decagon

6. hexagon

Use polygon ABCDEFG to answer each question.

7. Name the vertices of the polygon.

8. Name the angles of the polygon.

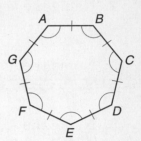

9. Name the sides of the polygon.

10. Is the polygon convex or concave.

11. Name the polygon according to the number of sides it has.

12. Is the polygon regular? Explain.

Find the sum of the measures of the interior angles of each convex polygon.

13. heptagon

14. octagon

15. 13-gon

The number of sides of a regular polygon is given. Find the measure of an interior and an exterior angle of the polygon.

16. 5

17. 9

18. 10

Geometry

Polygons

State the number of sides for each convex polygon.

1. quadrilateral **4**

2. octagon **8**

3. 83-gon **83**

4. heptagon **7**

5. decagon **10**

6. hexagon **6**

Use polygon ABCDEFG to answer each question.

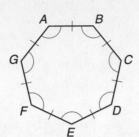

7. Name the vertices of the polygon. **A, B, C, D, E, F, G**

8. Name the angles of the polygon. **∠A, ∠B, ∠C, ∠D, ∠E, ∠F, ∠G**

9. Name the sides of the polygon. **$\overline{AB}$, $\overline{BC}$, $\overline{CD}$, $\overline{DE}$, $\overline{EF}$, $\overline{FG}$, GA**

10. Is the polygon convex or concave. **convex**

11. Name the polygon according to the number of sides it has. **heptagon**

12. Is the polygon regular? Explain. **Yes; its sides are all congruent, and its angles are all congruent, and it is convex.**

Find the sum of the measures of the interior angles of each convex polygon.

13. heptagon **900**

14. octagon **1080**

15. 13-gon **1980**

The number of sides of a regular polygon is given. Find the measure of an interior and an exterior angle of the polygon.

16. 5 **105, 72**

17. 9 **140, 40**

18. 10 **144, 36**

Practice

Tessellations

Determine whether each figure tessellates in a plane. If so, draw a sample figure.

1. scalene triangle

2. regular 18-gon

3. parallelogram

Determine if each pattern will tessellate.

4. octagon and isosceles triangle

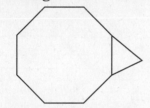

5. three isosceles triangles

6. isosceles trapezoid and square

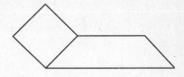

Determine whether each tessellation is regular, uniform, or semi-regular. Name all possibilities.

7. hexagon and triangle

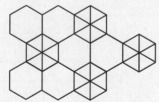

8. hexagon and triangle

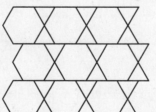

9. obtuse triangle

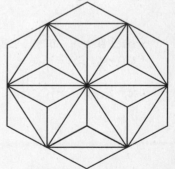

10. Guess and check Use the following three shapes and determine if they can tessellate a row. If so, draw a sample row.

NAME_____ DATE _____

Practice

Student Edition
Pages 523–527

Tessellations

Determine whether each figure tessellates in a plane. If so, draw a sample figure.

1. scalene triangle
Answers may vary.

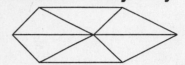

2. regular 18-gon
Does not tessellate.

3. parallelogram
Answers may vary.

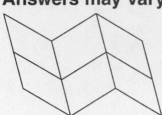

Determine if each pattern will tessellate.

4. octagon and isosceles triangle

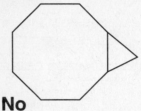

No

5. three isosceles triangles

Yes

6. isosceles trapezoid and square

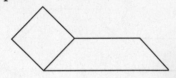

Yes

Determine whether each tessellation is regular, uniform, or semi-regular. Name all possibilities.

7. hexagon and triangle

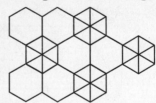

uniform, semi-regular

8. hexagon and triangle

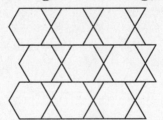

semi-regular

9. obtuse triangle

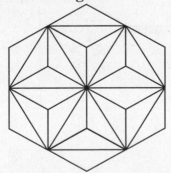

not uniform

10. Guess and check Use the following three shapes and determine if they can tessellate a row. If so, draw a sample row.

   yes;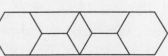

Area of Parallelograms

Find the area of each figure or shaded region. Assume that angles that appear to be right are right angles.

1.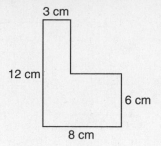

3 cm

12 cm

6 cm

8 cm

2.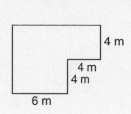

4 m

4 m
4 m

6 m

3.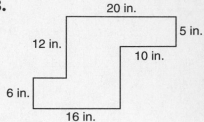

20 in.

5 in.

12 in.

10 in.

6 in.

16 in.

4.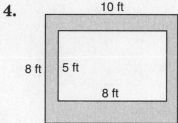

10 ft

8 ft   5 ft

8 ft

5.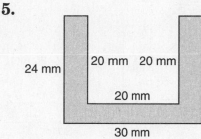

24 mm

20 mm   20 mm

20 mm

30 mm

6.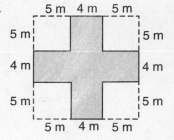

5 m   4 m   5 m

5 m   5 m

4 m   4 m

5 m   5 m

5 m   4 m   5 m

7. The sides of a parallelogram have lengths 8 inches and 16 inches and one of the angles of the parallelogram has a measure of 45°. Find the area of the parallelogram.

8. Find the area of the parallelogram that has vertices $A(0, 0)$, $B(2, 7)$, $C(10, 7)$, and $D(8, 0)$.

9. Find the area of the parallelogram that has vertices $W(-4, 15)$, $X(1, 15)$, $Y(4, 10)$, and $Z(-1, 10)$.

Area of Parallelograms

*Find the area of each figure or shaded region. Assume that
angles that appear to be right are right angles.*

1.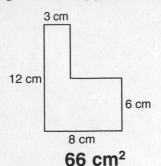

3 cm

12 cm

6 cm

8 cm

66 cm²

2.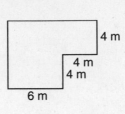

4 m

4 m
4 m

6 m

64 m²

3.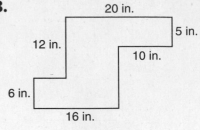

20 in.

5 in.

12 in.

10 in.

6 in.

16 in.

266 in²

4.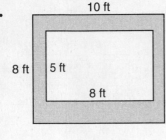

10 ft

8 ft   5 ft

8 ft

40 ft²

5.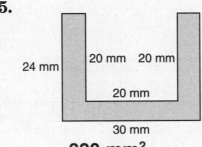

24 mm

20 mm   20 mm

20 mm

30 mm

320 mm²

6.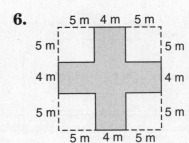

5 m 4 m 5 m

5 m   5 m

4 m   4 m

5 m   5 m

5 m 4 m 5 m

96 m²

7. The sides of a parallelogram have lengths 8 inches and
16 inches and one of the angles of the parallelogram has a
measure of 45°. Find the area of the parallelogram. **64√2 or about 90.5 in²**

8. Find the area of the parallelogram that has vertices $A(0, 0)$,
$B(2, 7)$, $C(10, 7)$, and $D(8, 0)$. **56 units²**

9. Find the area of the parallelogram that has vertices $W(-4, 15)$,
$X(1, 15)$, $Y(4, 10)$, and $Z(-1, 10)$. **25 units²**

Area of Triangles, Rhombi, and Trapezoids

Find each missing measure.

1. The area of a triangle is 216 square units. If the height is 18 units, what is the length of the base?

2. The diagonals of a rhombus are 21 and 16 centimeters long. Find the area of the rhombus.

3. The area of a trapezoid is 80 square units. If its height is 8 units, find the length of its median.

4. The height of a trapezoid is 9 cm. The bases are 8 cm and 12 cm long. Find the area.

5. A trapezoid has an area of 908.5 cm². If the altitude measures 23 cm and one base measures 36 cm, find the length of the other base.

6. The measure of the consecutive sides of an isosceles trapezoid are in the ratio 8:5:2:5. The perimeter of the trapezoid is 140 inches. If its height is 28 inches, find the area of the trapezoid.

Practice

Area of Triangles, Rhombi, and Trapezoids

Find each missing measure.

1. The area of a triangle is 216 square units. If the height is 18 units, what is the length of the base? **24 units**

2. The diagonals of a rhombus are 21 and 16 centimeters long. Find the area of the rhombus. **168 cm²**

3. The area of a trapezoid is 80 square units. If its height is 8 units, find the length of its median. **10 units**

4. The height of a trapezoid is 9 cm. The bases are 8 cm and 12 cm long. Find the area. **90 cm²**

5. A trapezoid has an area of 908.5 cm². If the altitude measures 23 cm and one base measures 36 cm, find the length of the other base. **43 cm**

6. The measure of the consecutive sides of an isosceles trapezoid are in the ratio 8:5:2:5. The perimeter of the trapezoid is 140 inches. If its height is 28 inches, find the area of the trapezoid. **980 in²**

NAME_____ DATE _____

Practice

Area of Regular Polygons and Circles

Find the area of each regular polygon. Round your answers to the nearest tenth.

1. an octagon with an apothem 4.8 centimeters long and a side 4 centimeters long

2. a square with a side 24 inches long and an apothem 12 inches long

3. a hexagon with a side 23.1 meters long and an apothem 20.0 meters long

4. a pentagon with an apothem 316.6 millimeters long and a side 460 millimeters long

Find the apothem, area, and perimeter of each regular polygon. Round your answers to the nearest tenth.

5.

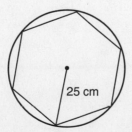

8 in.

6.

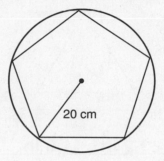

20 cm

7.

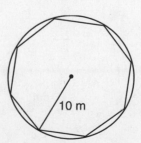

25 cm

8.

10 m

Geometry

NAME _____ DATE _____

Practice

Student Edition
Pages 543–550

Area of Regular Polygons and Circles

Find the area of each regular polygon. Round your answers to the nearest tenth.

1. an octagon with an apothem
   4.8 centimeters long and a side
   4 centimeters long **76.8 cm²**

2. a square with a side 24 inches long
   and an apothem 12 inches long
   576 in²

3. a hexagon with a side 23.1 meters
   long and an apothem 20.0 meters
   long **1386 m²**

4. a pentagon with an apothem
   316.6 millimeters long and a side
   460 millimeters long **364,090 mm²**

Find the apothem, area, and perimeter of each regular polygon. Round your answers to the nearest tenth.

5.

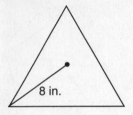

8 in.

4 in., 83.2 in², 41.6 in.

6.

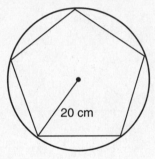

20 cm

16.2 cm, 952.6 cm², 117.6 cm

7.

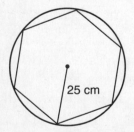

25 cm

21.7 cm, 1627.5 cm², 150 cm

8.

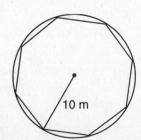

10 m

9.2 m, 281.5 m², 61.2 m

Geometry

Practice

Integration: Probability:
Geometric Probability

A point is chosen __at random__ on $\overline{AB}$. C is the midpoint of $\overline{AB}$, D is the midpoint of AC, and E is the midpoint of AD. Find each probability.

1. The point is on $\overline{AC}$.

2. The point is on $\overline{CB}$.

3. The point is on $\overline{AD}$.

4. The point is on $\overline{DB}$.

5. The point is on $\overline{ED}$.

6. The point is on $\overline{EC}$.

Find the probability that a point chosen at random in each figure lies in the shaded region.

7.

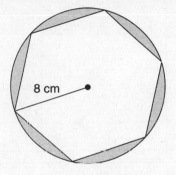

8.

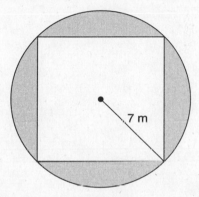

9.

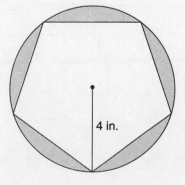

10.

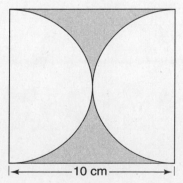

Geometry

Integration: Probability: Geometric Probability

A point is chosen at random on $\overline{AB}$. C is the midpoint of $\overline{AB}$, D is the midpoint of $\overline{AC}$, and E is the midpoint of $\overline{AD}$. Find each probability.

1. The point is on $\overline{AC}$. $\frac{1}{2}$

2. The point is on $\overline{CB}$. $\frac{1}{2}$

3. The point is on $\overline{AD}$. $\frac{1}{4}$

4. The point is on $\overline{DB}$. $\frac{3}{4}$

5. The point is on $\overline{ED}$. $\frac{1}{8}$

6. The point is on $\overline{EC}$. $\frac{3}{8}$

Find the probability that a point chosen at random in each figure lies in the shaded region.

7.

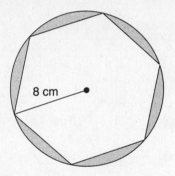

8 cm

0.17

8.

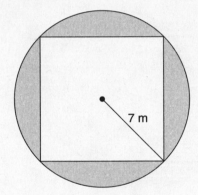

7 m

0.36

9.

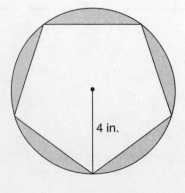

4 in.

0.24

10.

![square with two semicircles, 10 cm]

10 cm

0.21

Practice

Integration: Graph Theory
Polygons As Networks

Find the degree of each node in the network.

1.

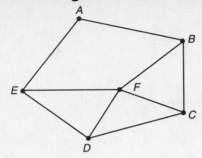

2.

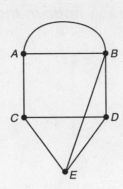

Name the edges that need to be added to make the network complete.

3.

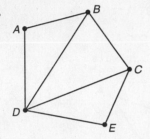

4.

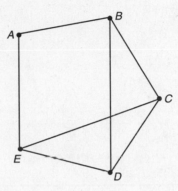

Determine whether each network is traceable. If a network is traceable, use arrows to trace the network.

5.

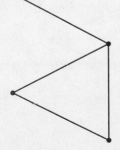

6.

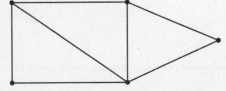

7. Draw two network of your own that are traceable. Then draw two networks that are not traceable.

NAME_____ DATE _____

Practice

Integration: Graph Theory
Polygons As Networks

Find the degree of each node in the network.

1.

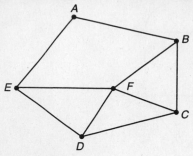

2.

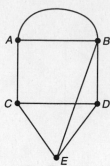

$A - 2, B - 3, C - 3, D - 3, E - 3, F - 4$ $A - 3, B - 4, C - 3, D - 3, E - 3$

Name the edges that need to be added to make the network complete.

3.

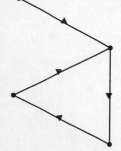

**edges between *A* and *C*,
A and *E*, and *B* and *E***

4.

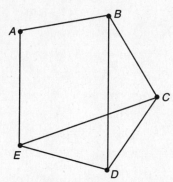

**edges between *A* and *C*,
A and *D*, and *B* and *E***

Determine whether each network is traceable. If a network is traceable, use arrows to trace the network.

5.

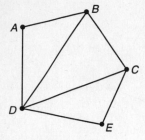

traceable

6.

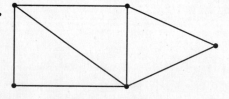

not traceable

7. Draw two network of your own that are traceable. Then draw
two networks that are not traceable. **See students' work.**

Student Edition
Pages 575–581

Practice

Exploring Three-Dimensional Figures

*Various views of a solid figure are given below. The edge of
one block represents one unit of length. A dark segment
indicates a break in the surface. Make a model of each figure.
Then draw the back view of the figure.*

top view	left view	front view	right view	back view

1.

2.

3.

4.

From the views shown in Exercises 1–4, draw a corner view.

5.

6.

7.

8.

NAME _____ DATE _____

Practice

Student Edition
Pages 575–581

Exploring Three-Dimensional Figures

Various views of a solid figure are given below. The edge of one block represents one unit of length. A dark segment indicates a break in the surface. Make a model of each figure. Then draw the back view of the figure.

top view	left view	front view	right view	back view

1.

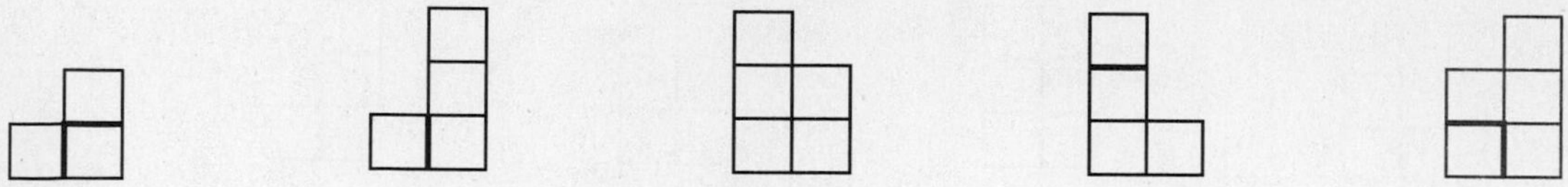

2.

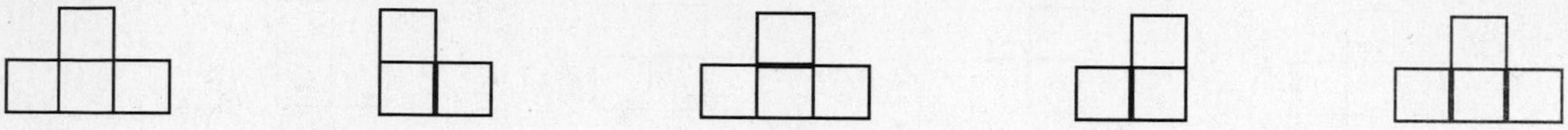

3.

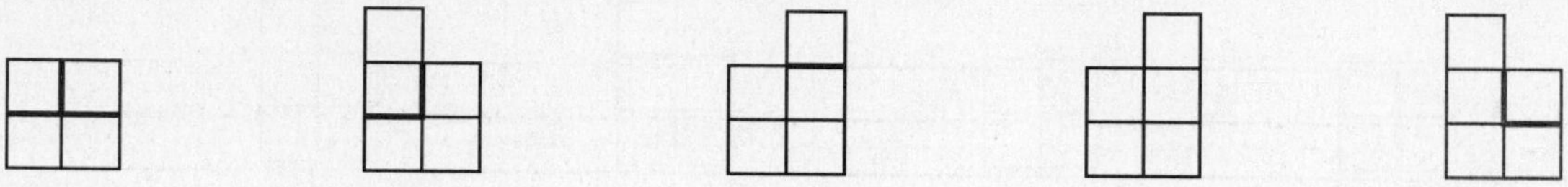

4.

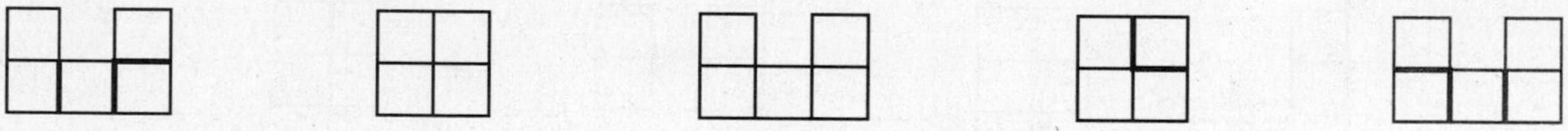

From the views shown in Exercises 1–4, draw a corner view.

5.

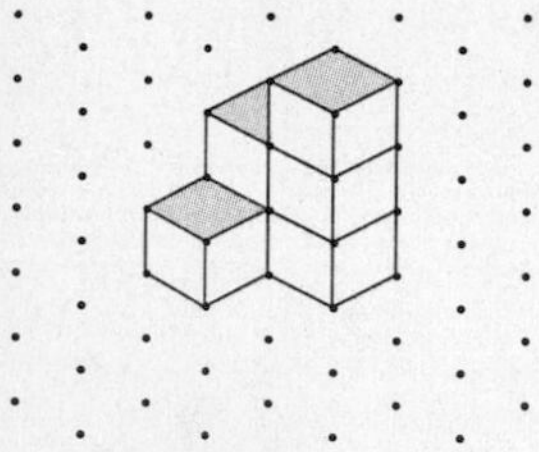

6.

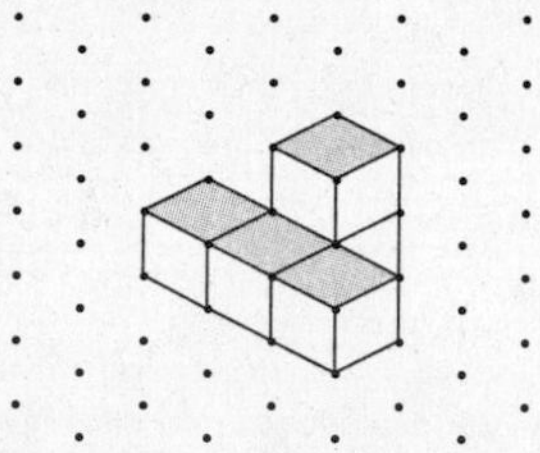

7.

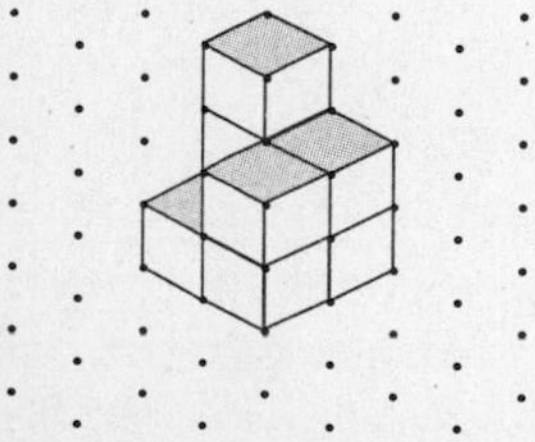

8.

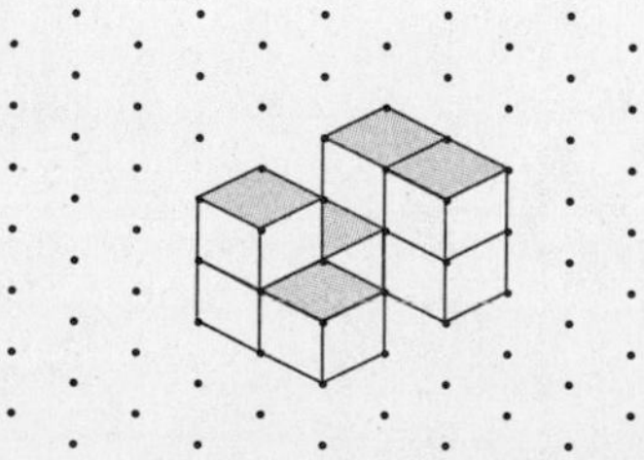

T64

Geometry

NAME_____ DATE _____

Practice

Student Edition
Pages 584–589

Nets and Surface Area

Given each polyhedron, label the remaining vertices of its net.

1.

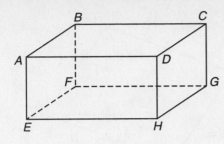

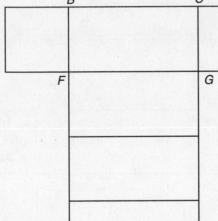

2.

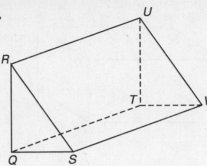

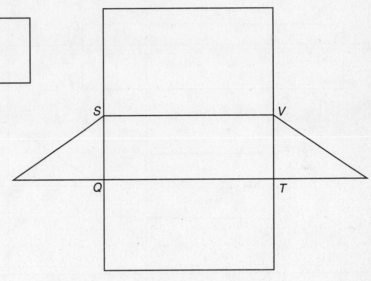

Identify the number and type of polygons that are faces in each polyhedron.

3.

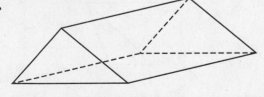

4.

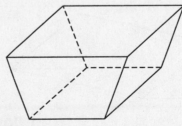

5.

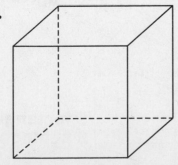

6.

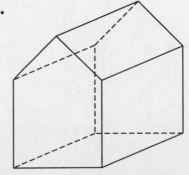

65

Geometry

NAME_____ DATE _____

Practice

Nets and Surface Area

Given each polyhedron, label the remaining vertices of its net.

1.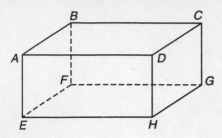

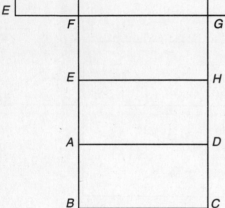

2.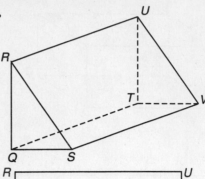

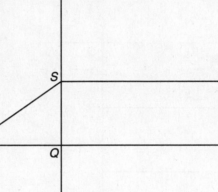

Identify the number and type of polygons that are faces in each polyhedron.

3.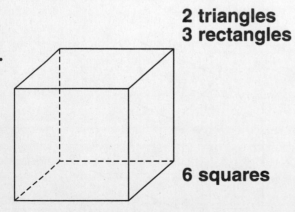

**2 triangles
3 rectangles**

4.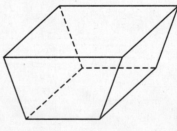

**4 rectangles
2 trapezoids**

5.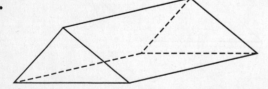

6 squares

6.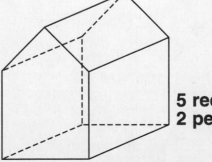

**5 rectangles
2 pentagons**

NAME_____ DATE _____

Practice

Student Edition
Pages 591–598

Surface Area of Prisms and Cylinders

**Use the right cylinders shown to answer each of the following.
Express all answers in terms of π.**

1. Find the circumference of the base.

2. Find the lateral area.

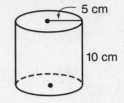

3. Find the area of a base.

4. Find the surface area.

5. Find the circumference of the base.

6. Find the lateral area.

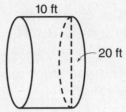

7. Find the area of a base.

8. Find the surface area.

**Find the lateral area and the surface area of each right prism.
Round to the nearest tenth.**

9.

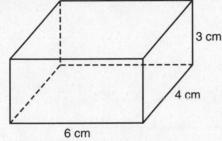

10.

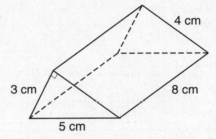

11.

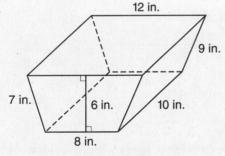

12.

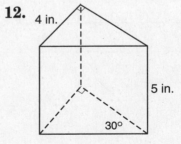

13.

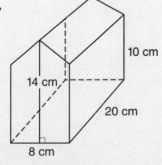

14.

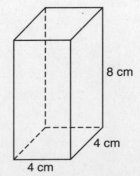

Geometry

Surface Area of Prisms and Cylinders

Use the right cylinders shown to answer each of the following.
Express all answers in terms of π.

1. Find the circumference of the base. **10π cm**

2. Find the lateral area. **100π cm²**

3. Find the area of a base. **25π cm²**

4. Find the surface area. **150π cm²**

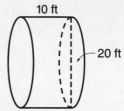

5. Find the circumference of the base. **20π ft**

6. Find the lateral area. **200π ft²**

7. Find the area of a base. **100π ft²**

8. Find the surface area. **400π ft²**

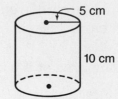

Find the lateral area and the surface area of each right prism.
Round to the nearest tenth.

9.

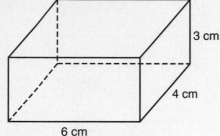

60 cm², 108 cm²

10.

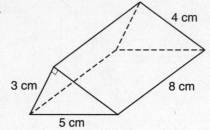

96 cm², 108 cm²

11.

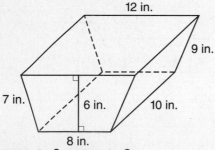

360 in², 480 in²

12.

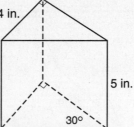

94.6 in², 122.4 in²

13.

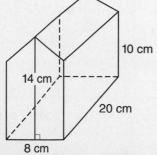

786.3 cm², 978.3 cm²

14.

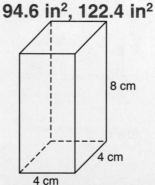

128 cm², 160 cm²

Surface Area of Pyramids and Cones

**Find the lateral area of each regular pyramid or right cone.
Round to the nearest tenth.**

1.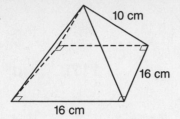
   10 cm
   16 cm
   16 cm

2.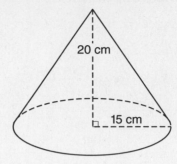
   20 cm
   15 cm

3.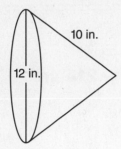
   10 in.
   12 in.

4.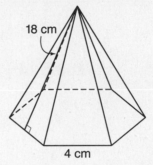
   18 cm
   4 cm

**Find the surface area of each solid. Round to the nearest
tenth.**

5.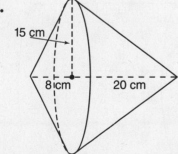
   15 cm
   8 cm   20 cm

6.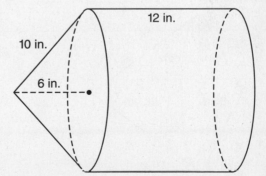
   12 in.
   10 in.
   6 in.

Practice

Surface Area of Pyramids and Cones

Find the lateral area of each regular pyramid or right cone.
Round to the nearest tenth.

1.

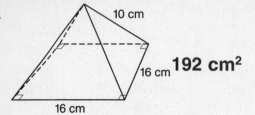

10 cm

16 cm **192 cm²**

16 cm

2.

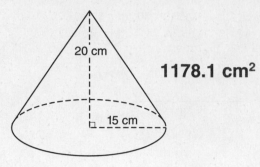

20 cm

15 cm

1178.1 cm²

3.

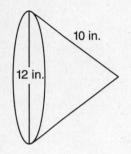

10 in.

12 in.

188.5 in²

4.

18 cm

4 cm

216 cm²

Find the surface area of each solid. Round to the nearest tenth.

5.

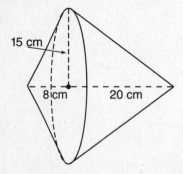

15 cm

8 cm   20 cm

1979.2 cm²

6.

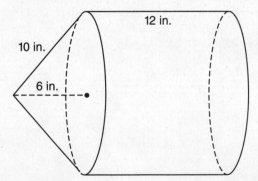

12 in.

10 in.

6 in.

1055.6 in²

Geometry

Volume of Prisms and Cylinders

Find each of the following. Round to the nearest tenth.

1. the volume of a right prism whose square base has sides of 4 feet and whose height is 9 feet

2. the volume of a cylinder with a height of 2 meters and a radius of 0.5 meters

Find the volume of each solid. Round to the nearest tenth.

3.

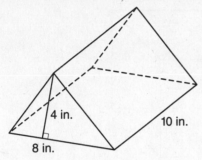

4 in.
10 in.
8 in.

4.

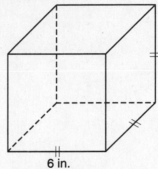

6 in.

5.

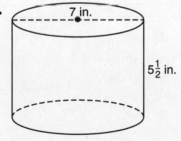

7 in.
$5\frac{1}{2}$ in.

6.

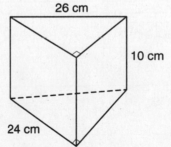

26 cm
10 cm
24 cm

7.

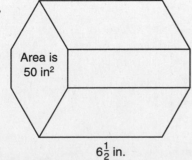

Area is 50 in²
$6\frac{1}{2}$ in.

8. Hole

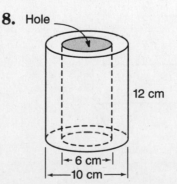

12 cm
|← 6 cm →|
—— 10 cm ——|

Geometry

Practice

Volume of Prisms and Cylinders

Find each of the following. Round to the nearest tenth.

1. the volume of a right prism whose square base has sides of 4 feet and whose height is 9 feet **144.0 ft³**

2. the volume of a cylinder with a height of 2 meters and a radius of 0.5 meters **1.6 m³**

Find the volume of each solid. Round to the nearest tenth.

3.
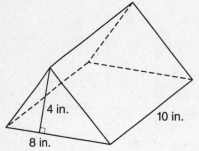
4 in.
8 in.
10 in.
160 in³

4.
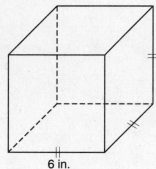
6 in.
216 in³

5.
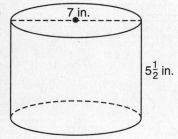
7 in.
$5\frac{1}{2}$ in.
211.7 in³

6.
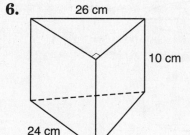
26 cm
10 cm
24 cm
1200 cm³

7.
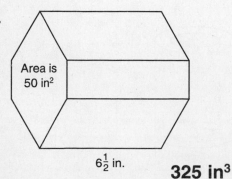
Area is 50 in²
$6\frac{1}{2}$ in.
325 in³

8. Hole
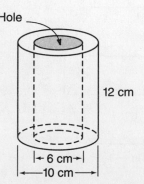
12 cm
|←6 cm→|
|←——10 cm——→|
603.2 cm³

Geometry

Practice

Volume of Pyramids and Cones

Find the volume of each pyramid. Round to the nearest tenth.

1. The base has an area of 84.3 square centimeters, and the height is 16.4 centimeters

2. The base has an area of 17 square feet, and the height is 3 feet.

Find the volume of each cone. Round to the nearest tenth.

3. The base has a radius of 16 centimeters, and the height is 12 centimeters

4. The base has a diameter of 24 meters, and the height is 15.3 meters

Find the volume of each solid. Round to the nearest tenth.

5.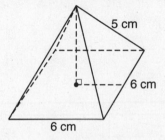

6.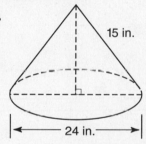

7.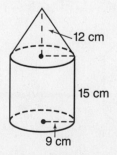

8.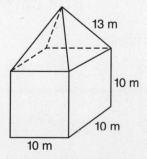

NAME_____ DATE _____

Practice

Student Edition
Pages 615–620

Volume of Pyramids and Cones

Find the volume of each pyramid. Round to the nearest tenth.

1. The base has an area of
84.3 square centimeters, and
the height is 16.4 centimeters
460.8 cm³

2. The base has an area of 17 square
feet, and the height is 3 feet.
17.0 ft³

Find the volume of each cone. Round to the nearest tenth.

3. The base has a radius of
16 centimeters, and the height
is 12 centimeters **3217.0 cm³**

4. The base has a diameter of
24 meters, and the height is
15.3 meters **2307.2 m³**

Find the volume of each solid. Round to the nearest tenth.

5.

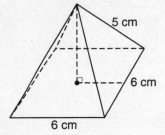

5 cm
6 cm
6 cm

6.

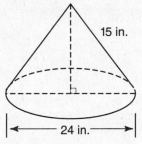

15 in.
24 in.

31.7 cm³

1357.2 in³

7.

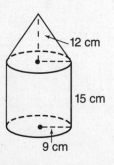

12 cm
15 cm
9 cm

8.

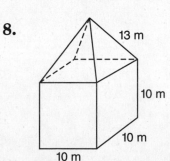

13 m
10 m
10 m
10 m

4834.9 cm³

1363.6 m³

Practice

Surface Area and Volume of Spheres

Find the surface area and volume of each sphere described below. Round to the nearest tenth.

1. The diameter is 100 centimeters.

2. A great circle has a circumference 83.92 meters.

3. The radius is 12 inches long.

4. A great circle has an area of 70.58 square feet.

Find the surface area and volume of each solid. Round to the nearest tenth.

5.

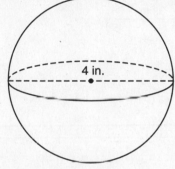

4 in.

6.

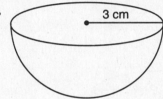

3 cm

7.

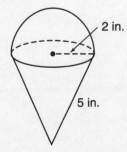

2 in.

5 in.

8.

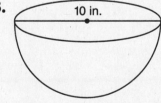

10 in.

NAME_____ DATE _____

Practice

Surface Area and Volume of Spheres

Find the surface area and volume of each sphere described below. Round to the nearest tenth.

1. The diameter is 100 centimeters. **31,415.9 cm^2; 523,598.8 cm^3**

2. A great circle has a circumference 83.92 meters. **2241.7 m^2; 9980.3 m^3**

3. The radius is 12 inches long. **1809.6 in^2; 7238.2 in^3**

4. A great circle has an area of 70.58 square feet. **282.3 ft^2; 446.1 ft^3**

Find the surface area and volume of each solid. Round to the nearest tenth.

5.

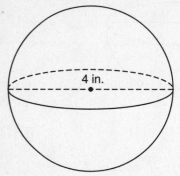

4 in.

50.3 in^2, 33.5 in^3

6.

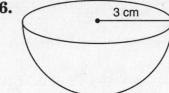

3 cm

84.8 cm^2, 56.5 cm^3

7.

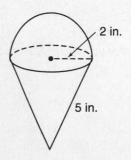

2 in.

5 in.

56.5 in^2, 36.0 in^3

8.

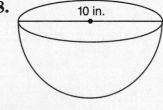

10 in.

235.6 in^2, 261.8 in^3

Geometry

Congruent and Similar Solids

Determine if each pair of solids is <u>similar</u>, <u>congruent</u>, or <u>neither</u>.

1.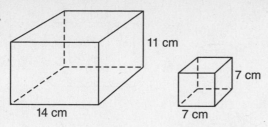

2.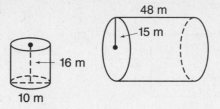

3.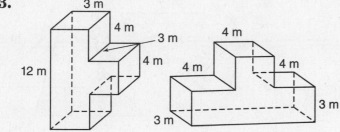

4.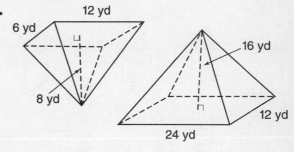

The two right rectangular prisms shown at the right are similar.

5. Find the ratio of the perimeters of the bases.

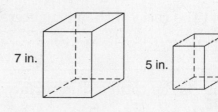

6. What is the ratio of the surface areas?

7. Suppose the volume of the smaller prism is 60 in³.
Find the volume of the larger prism.

Determine if each statement is <u>true</u> or <u>false</u>. If the statement is false, rewrite it so that it is true.

8. If two cylinders are similar, then their volumes are equal.

9. Doubling the height of a cylinder doubles the volume.

10. Two solids are congruent if they have the same shape.

NAME _____ DATE _____

Practice

Student Edition
Pages 629–635

Congruent and Similar Solids

Determine if each pair of solids is <u>similar</u>, <u>congruent</u>, or <u>neither</u>.

1.

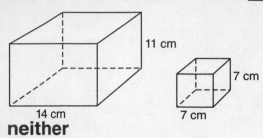

11 cm

7 cm

14 cm   7 cm

neither

2.

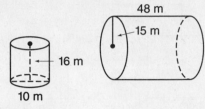

48 m

15 m

16 m

10 m

similar

3.

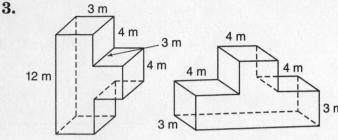

3 m   4 m   3 m   4 m

12 m   4 m   4 m   4 m

3 m   3 m

congruent

4.

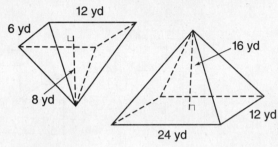

12 yd   6 yd   16 yd

8 yd   24 yd   12 yd

similar

The two right rectangular prisms shown at the right are similar.

5. Find the ratio of the perimeters of the bases.
$\dfrac{7}{5}$

6. What is the ratio of the surface areas?
$\dfrac{49}{25}$

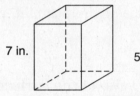

7 in.   5 in.

7. Suppose the volume of the smaller prism is 60 in³.
Find the volume of the larger prism. **84 in³**

Determine if each statement is <u>true</u> or <u>false</u>. If the statement is false, rewrite it so that it is true.

8. If two cylinders are similar, then their volumes are equal.
False; if two cylinders are congruent, then their volumes are equal.

9. Doubling the height of a cylinder doubles the volume. **True**

10. Two solids are congruent if they have the same shape.
False; two solids are congruent if they have the same shape and size.

NAME_____ DATE _____

Practice

Student Edition
Pages 646–651

Integration: Algebra
Graphing Linear Equations

Graph each pair of linear equations on the same coordinate plane. Determine if the lines are <u>parallel</u>, <u>perpendicular</u>, or <u>neither</u> by finding the slope of each line.

1. $y = x + 2$
$y - x = 4$

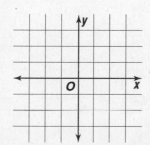

2. $2x - y = 3$
$y = 2x + 4$

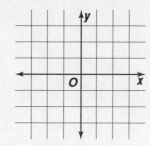

3. $3y = x + 1$
$y = -3x + 2$

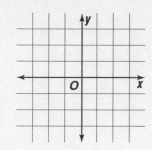

4. $y = 2x + 1$
$y = 3x - 1$

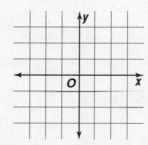

Find the slope and y-intercept of the graph of each equation.

5. $x + y = 8$ **6.** $2x - y = 4$ **7.** $2x - 3y = 10$

Determine the x- and y-intercepts of each line. Then graph the equation.

8. $y = 2x - 3$

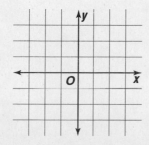

9. $y = 5$

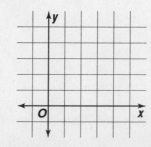

NAME_____ DATE _____

Practice

Integration: Algebra
Graphing Linear Equations

Graph each pair of linear equations on the same coordinate plane. Determine if the lines are <u>parallel</u>, <u>perpendicular</u>, or <u>neither</u> by finding the slope of each line.

1. $y = x + 2$ **parallel; 1, 1**
$y - x = 4$

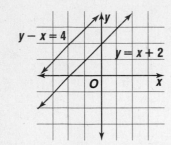

2. $2x - y = 3$ **parallel; 2, 2**
$y = 2x + 4$

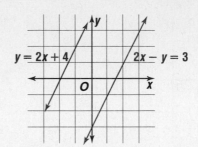

3. $3y = x + 1$ **perpendicular;**
$y = -3x + 2$ **$\frac{1}{3}$, -3**

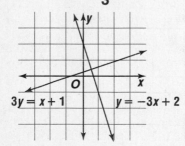

4. $y = 2x + 1$ **neither; 2, 3**
$y = 3x - 1$

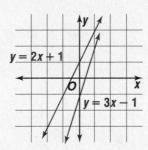

Find the slope and y-intercept of the graph of each equation.

5. $x + y = 8$
-1, 8

6. $2x - y = 4$
2, -4

7. $2x - 3y = 10$
$\frac{2}{3}$, $-\frac{10}{3}$

Determine the x- and y-intercepts of each line. Then graph the equation.

8. $y = 2x - 3$

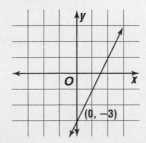

$\frac{3}{2}$, **-3**

9. $y = 5$

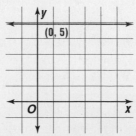

no x-intercept, 5

 Geometry

Practice

Integration: Algebra
Writing Equations of Lines

*State the slope and y-intercept for each line. Then write the
equation of the line in slope-intercept form.*

1. $\overrightarrow{AB}$

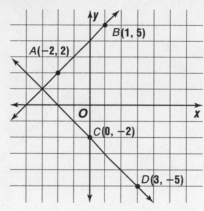

2. $\overrightarrow{CD}$

*Write the equation in slope-intercept form of the line
satisfying the given conditions.*

3. parallel to $y = 3x - 2$; y-intercept $= 1$

4. perpendicular to $y = \frac{1}{2}x + 8$; passes through the point at $(0, 3)$

5. perpendicular to the line passing through points at $(-2, 3)$
   and $(2, 1)$; y-intercept $= -3$

6. passes through the points at $(1, 5)$ and $(-3, 5)$

7. x-intercept $= 5$; y-intercept $= -2$

8. $m = -\frac{2}{3}$; passes through the point at $(-1, 2)$

9. $m = -4$; x-intercept $= 0$

10. The length of a rectangular garden is 30 feet more than
    2 times its width. Its perimeter is 300 feet. Find its length
    and width.

NAME_____ DATE _____

Practice

Integration: Algebra
Writing Equations of Lines

State the slope and y-intercept for each line. Then write the equation of the line in slope-intercept form.

1. $\overleftrightarrow{AB}$ **1, 4,** $y = x + 4$

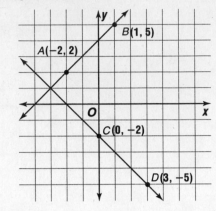

2. $\overleftrightarrow{CD}$ **-1, -2,** $y = -x - 2$

Write the equation in slope-intercept form of the line satisfying the given conditions.

3. parallel to $y = 3x - 2$; y-intercept $= 1$ $y = 3x + 1$

4. perpendicular to $y = \frac{1}{2}x + 8$; passes through the point at (0, 3)
   $y = -2x + 3$

5. perpendicular to the line passing through points at (-2, 3) and (2, 1); y-intercept $= -3$ $y = 2x - 3$

6. passes through the points at (1, 5) and (-3, 5) $y = 5$

7. x-intercept $= 5$; y-intercept $= -2$ $y = \frac{2}{5}x - 2$

8. $m = -\frac{2}{3}$; passes through the point at (-1, 2) $y = -\frac{2}{3}x + \frac{4}{3}$

9. $m = -4$; x-intercept $= 0$ $y = -4x$

10. The length of a rectangular garden is 30 feet more than 2 times its width. Its perimeter is 300 feet. Find its length and width. **110 feet, 40 feet**

Practice

Integration: Algebra and Statistics
Scatter Plots and Slope

1. **Travel**   The table below lists the number
   of gallons of gasoline used during 5 different
   trips.

Length of trip (in miles)	374	506	2020	144	1034
Gallons of gasoline	17	22	101	6	47

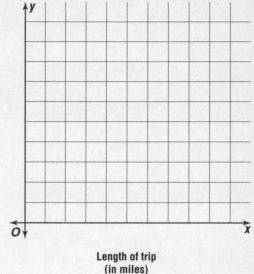

Gallons
of
gasoline

Length of trip
(in miles)

   a. Draw a scatter plot to show how the
      length of the trip x and the gallons of
      gasoline y are related.

   b. Write an equation that relates the trip
      length to the gallons of gasoline used.

   c. About how many gallons of gasoline will be used on an
      800-mile trip?

2. Find the equation of the line that is the
   perpendicular bisector of the segment
   whose endpoints are $(3, 7)$ and $(-3, -1)$.

3. Find the equations of the lines that
   contain sides of an isosceles triangle if
   the vertex of the vertex angle is at the
   y-intercept of $y = -2x + 3$ and the
   vertex of a base angle is at $(6, 1)$.

The vertices of $\triangle DEF$ are D(0, 12), E($-$2, 10), and F(4, 6).

4. Write the equation of the line that
   contains the altitude to $\overline{EF}$.

5. Write the equation of the line line that
   contains the perpendicular bisector to
   $\overline{ED}$.

Practice

Integration: Algebra and Statistics
Scatter Plots and Slope

1. **Travel** The table below lists the number of gallons of gasoline used during 5 different trips.

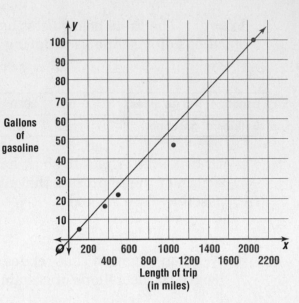

Length of trip (in miles)	374	506	2020	144	1034
Gallons of gasoline	17	22	101	6	47

a. Draw a scatter plot to show how the length of the trip x and the gallons of gasoline y are related.

b. Write an equation that relates the trip length to the gallons of gasoline used.
Sample answer: $y = \dfrac{1}{22}x$

c. About how many gallons of gasoline will be used on an 800-mile trip? **36 gallons**

2. Find the equation of the line that is the perpendicular bisector of the segment whose endpoints are (3, 7) and (-3, -1).
$y = -\dfrac{3}{4}x + 3$

3. Find the equations of the lines that contain sides of an isosceles triangle if the vertex of the vertex angle is at the y-intercept of $y = -2x + 3$ and the vertex of a base angle is at (6, 1).
$y = 1, \ y = \dfrac{1}{3}x + 3, \ y = -\dfrac{1}{3}x + 3$ or
$x = 6, \ y = \dfrac{1}{3}x + 3, \ y = -\dfrac{1}{3}x + 3$

The vertices of △DEF are D(0, 12), E(-2, 10), and F(4, 6).

4. Write the equation of the line that contains the altitude to $\overline{EF}$.
$y = \dfrac{3}{2}x + 12$

5. Write the equation of the line line that contains the perpendicular bisector to $\overline{ED}$. $y = -x + 10$

NAME_____ DATE _____

Practice

Coordinate Proof

Name the missing coordinates in terms of the given variables.

1. $\triangle XYZ$ is isosceles and right.

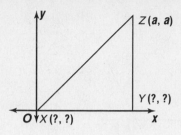

2. *MART* is a rhombus.

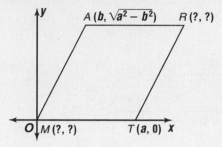

3. *RECT* is a rectangle.

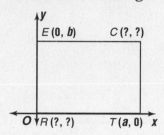

4. *DEFG* is a parallelogram.

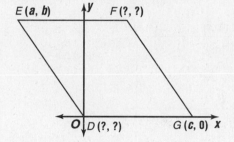

5. Use a coordinate proof to prove that the diagonals of a rhombus are perpendicular. Draw the diagram at the right.

75

Practice

Student Edition
Pages 666–671

Coordinate Proof

Name the missing coordinates in terms of the given variables.

1. $\triangle XYZ$ is isosceles and right.

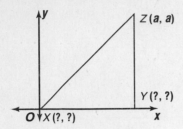

X(0, 0) Y(a, 0)

2. *MART* is a rhombus.

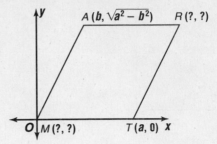

M(0, 0), R(a + b, $\sqrt{a^2 - b^2}$)

3. *RECT* is a rectangle.

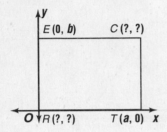

R(0, 0) C(a, b)

4. *DEFG* is a parallelogram.

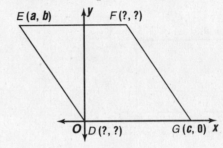

D(0, 0), F(a + c, b)

5. Use a coordinate proof to prove that the diagonals of a rhombus are perpendicular. Draw the diagram at the right.

Typical proof:

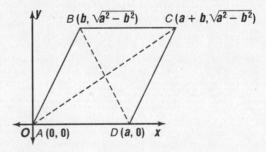

$$\text{slope of } \overline{AC} = \frac{\sqrt{a^2 - b^2} - 0}{a + b - 0} = \frac{\sqrt{a^2 - b^2}}{a + b}$$

$$\text{slope of } \overline{BD} = \frac{\sqrt{a^2 - b^2} - 0}{b - a} = \frac{\sqrt{a^2 - b^2}}{b - a}$$

$$\frac{\sqrt{a^2 - b^2}}{a + b} \cdot \frac{\sqrt{a^2 - b^2}}{b - a} = \frac{a^2 - b^2}{b^2 - a^2} = -1$$

Practice

Vectors

Given $\vec{a}$ = (8, 6), $\vec{b}$ = (4, 3), $\vec{c}$ = (1, 2), and $\vec{d}$ = (-3, -6), answer each of the following.

1. Find the magnitude of $\vec{a}$.

2. Find the magnitude $\vec{c}$.

3. Determine if $\vec{b}$ and $\vec{d}$ are equal.

4. Determine if $\vec{c}$ and $\vec{d}$ are equal.

5. Find the coordinates of $\vec{a} + \vec{b}$.

6. Find the coordinates of $(\vec{b} + \vec{c}) + \vec{d}$.

7. Given $A(2, 5)$ and $B(7, 10)$, find the magnitude and direction of $\overrightarrow{AB}$.

8. Given $C(0, 1)$ and $D(8, 12)$, find the magnitude and direction of $\overrightarrow{CD}$.

Given path from A south 5 units to B, then east 12 units to C, answer each question.

9. What is the total length of the path?

10. What is the magnitude of $\overrightarrow{AC}$?

Practice

Vectors

Given $\vec{a}$ = (8, 6), $\vec{b}$ = (4, 3), $\vec{c}$ = (1, 2), and $\vec{d}$ = (-3, -6), answer each of the following.

1. Find the magnitude of $\vec{a}$. **10**

2. Find the magnitude $\vec{c}$. $\sqrt{5} \approx$ **2.2**

3. Determine if $\vec{b}$ and $\vec{d}$ are equal. **no**

4. Determine if $\vec{c}$ and $\vec{d}$ are equal. **no**

5. Find the coordinates of $\vec{a} + \vec{b}$. **(12, 9)**

6. Find the coordinates of $(\vec{b} + \vec{c}) + \vec{d}$.
(2, -1)

7. Given $A(2, 5)$ and $B(7, 10)$, find the magnitude and direction of $\overrightarrow{AB}$.
$\sqrt{50} \approx$ **7.1, 45°**

8. Given $C(0, 1)$ and $D(8, 12)$, find the magnitude and direction of $\overrightarrow{CD}$.
$\sqrt{185} \approx$ **13.6, about 54°**

Given path from A south 5 units to B, then east 12 units to C, answer each question.

9. What is the total length of the path?
17 units

10. What is the magnitude of $\overrightarrow{AC}$?
13 units

NAME_____ DATE _____

Practice

Coordinates in Space

Determine the distance between each pair of points.

1. $A(0, 0, 0)$ and $B(1, 2, 3)$

2. $C(4, -2, 3)$ and $D(0, 2, 0)$

3. $E(1, -2, 5)$ and $F(1, 2, 5)$

4. $P(0, 1, 0)$ and $Q(-1, 0, 1)$

Determine the coordinates of the midpoint of each line segment whose endpoints are given.

5. $A(0, 0, 4)$, $B(4, -6, 6)$

6. $C(-1, 2, 4)$, $D(3, -6, 8)$

7. $E(-2, -3, 6)$, $F(0, -6, 8)$

8. $G\left(-1, 5, \frac{3}{2}\right)$, $H\left(1, -5, \frac{1}{2}\right)$

Write an equation of the sphere given the coordinates of the center and the measure of the radius.

9. $C(0, -3, 1)$, $r = 3$

10. $C(-2, 1, 3)$, $r = 1\frac{1}{2}$

11. $C(3, 0, -1)$, $r = \dfrac{\sqrt{2}}{2}$

12. $C(5, 5, 5)$, $r = 7$

13. Find the perimeter of a triangle whose vertices are $A(0, 2, 1)$, $B(-2, 2, 6)$, and $C(4, 2, -2)$.

The diameter of a sphere has endpoints $A(-3, 2, 4)$ and $B(1, -6, 5)$.

14. Determine the center of the sphere.

15. Determine the radius of the sphere.

16. Write the equation of the sphere.

17. Find the surface area of the sphere.

Coordinates in Space

Determine the distance between each pair of points.

1. $A(0, 0, 0)$ and $B(1, 2, 3)$ $\sqrt{14} \approx$ **3.7**

2. $C(4, -2, 3)$ and $D(0, 2, 0)$ $\sqrt{41} \approx$ **6.4**

3. $E(1, -2, 5)$ and $F(1, 2, 5)$ **4**

4. $P(0, 1, 0)$ and $Q(-1, 0, 1)$ $\sqrt{3} \approx$ **1.7**

Determine the coordinates of the midpoint of each line segment whose endpoints are given.

5. $A(0, 0, 4)$, $B(4, -6, 6)$ **(2, -3, 5)**

6. $C(-1, 2, 4)$, $D(3, -6, 8)$ **(1, -2, 6)**

7. $E(-2, -3, 6)$, $F(0, -6, 8)$ $\left(\mathbf{-1}, -\frac{\mathbf{9}}{\mathbf{2}}, \mathbf{7}\right)$

8. $G\left(-1, 5, \frac{3}{2}\right)$, $H\left(1, -5, \frac{1}{2}\right)$ **(0, 0, 1)**

Write an equation of the sphere given the coordinates of the center and the measure of the radius.

9. $C(0, -3, 1)$, $r = 3$
$$x^2 + (y + 3)^2 + (z - 1)^2 = 9$$

10. $C(-2, 1, 3)$, $r = 1\frac{1}{2}$
$$(x + 2)^2 + (y - 1)^2 + (z - 3)^2 = \frac{9}{4}$$

11. $C(3, 0, -1)$, $r = \frac{\sqrt{2}}{2}$
$$(x - 3)^2 + y^2 + (z + 1)^2 = \frac{1}{2}$$

12. $C(5, 5, 5)$, $r = 7$
$$(x - 5)^2 + (y - 5)^2 + (z - 5)^2 = 49$$

13. Find the perimeter of a triangle whose vertices are $A(0, 2, 1)$, $B(-2, 2, 6)$, and $C(4, 2, -2)$. **15 + $\sqrt{29}$ units**

The diameter of a sphere has endpoints A(-3, 2, 4) and B(1, -6, 5).

14. Determine the center of the sphere.
(-1, -2, 4.5)

15. Determine the radius of the sphere.
4.5 units

16. Write the equation of the sphere.
$$(x + 1)^2 + (y + 2)^2 + (z - 4.5)^2 =$$
20.25

17. Find the surface area of the sphere.
**81π square units
or about 254.5 square units**

Practice

What Is Locus?

Draw a figure and describe the locus of points that satisfy each set of conditions.

1. all points in a plane that are midpoints of the radii of a given circle

2. all points in a plane that are equidistant from the endpoints of a given segment

3. all points in a plane that are equidistant from two parallel lines 12 centimeters apart

4. all points in a plane that are 4 centimeters away from $\overleftrightarrow{AB}$

5. all points in a plane that are equidistant from two concentric circles whose radii are 8 inches and 12 inches

6. all points in a plane that are centers of circles having a given line segment as a chord

7. all points in a plane that belong to a given angle or its interior and are equidistant from the sides of the given angle

NAME_____ DATE _____

Practice

What Is Locus?

Draw a figure and describe the locus of points that satisfy each set of conditions.

1. all points in a plane that are midpoints of the radii of a given circle

a circle whose radius is half the length of the radius of the given circle

2. all points in a plane that are equidistant from the endpoints of a given segment

the perpendicular bisector of the segment

3. all points in a plane that are equidistant from two parallel lines 12 centimeters apart

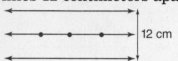

12 cm

a line that is between the two given lines and 6 cm from each

4. all points in a plane that are 4 centimeters away from $\overleftrightarrow{AB}$

4 cm

4 cm

A   B

a pair of lines parallel to $\overrightarrow{AB}$, one on each side of $\overrightarrow{AB}$ and 4 cm from $\overrightarrow{AB}$

5. all points in a plane that are equidistant from two concentric circles whose radii are 8 inches and 12 inches

12 in.

8 in.

a circle of radius 10, concentric with the given circles

6. all points in a plane that are centers of circles having a given line segment as a chord

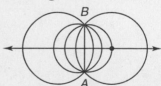

B

A

the perpendicular bisector of the line segment

7. all points in a plane that belong to a given angle or its interior and are equidistant from the sides of the given angle

the angle bisector

13-2

Practice

Locus and Systems of Equations

Graph each pair of equations to find the locus of points that satisfy both equations.

1. $x + y = 3$
    $x - y = 1$

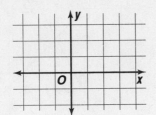

2. $y = 3 + x$
    $x + y = 5$

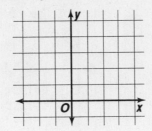

3. $y = 2x$
    $x + y = 3$

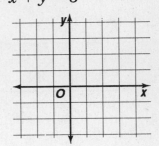

Use either substitution or elimination to find the locus of points that satisfy both equations.

4. $x + y = 7$
    $x - y = 9$

5. $x + y = 3$
    $3x - 5y = 17$

6. $y = 2x$
    $3x + y = 5$

7. $4x - 3y = -1$
    $x + 1 = y$

8. $2x + 3y = -1$
    $3x + 5y = -2$

9. $3y = 2 - x$
    $2x = 7 - 3y$

10. $y = 2x + 1$
     $y = 4x + 7$

11. $x = 4$
     $y = 3x - 5$

12. $3x + 2y = 10$
     $6x - 3y = 6$

Geometry

NAME_____ DATE _____

Practice

Locus and Systems of Equations

Graph each pair of equations to find the locus of points that satisfy both equations.

1. $x + y = 3$
$x - y = 1$

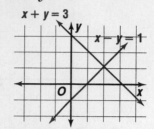

(2, 1)

2. $y = 3 + x$
$x + y = 5$

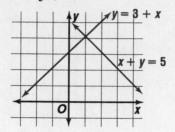

(1, 4)

3. $y = 2x$
$x + y = 3$

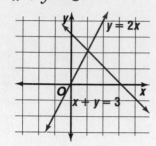

(1, 2)

Use either substitution or elimination to find the locus of points that satisfy both equations.

4. $x + y = 7$
$x - y = 9$ **(8, –1)**

5. $x + y = 3$
$3x - 5y = 17$ **(4, –1)**

6. $y = 2x$
$3x + y = 5$ **(1, 2)**

7. $4x - 3y = -1$
$x + 1 = y$ **(2, 3)**

8. $2x + 3y = -1$
$3x + 5y = -2$ **(1, –1)**

9. $3y = 2 - x$
$2x = 7 - 3y$ **(5, –1)**

10. $y = 2x + 1$
$y = 4x + 7$ **(–3, –5)**

11. $x = 4$
$y = 3x - 5$ **(4, 7)**

12. $3x + 2y = 10$
$6x - 3y = 6$ **(2, 2)**

13-3

Practice

Intersection of Loci

Describe the locus of points in a plane that satisfy each condition.

1. $x + y = 4$

2. $x = y$

3. $y = 5$

4. $x^2 + (y - 2)^2 = 25$

Describe the geometric figure whose locus in space satisfies each condition.

5. $(x + 2)^2 + (y - 3)^2 + z^2 = 64$

6. $(x - 2)^2 \, (y + 3)^2 + (z - 1)^2 = 81$

Draw a diagram and describe the locus of points.

7. all points in a plane that are 3 inches from a given segment and equidistant from the two endpoints

8. all points in a plane that are 3 inches from a given line and 3 inches from a given point on the line

9. all points in a plane that are equidistant from the vertices of a given square

10. all points in a plane that are 5 centimeters from a given point A and equidistant from points A and B that are 8 centimeters apart

Practice

Intersection of Loci

Describe the locus of points in a plane that satisfy each condition.

1. $x + y = 4$ **a line with slope -1 that passes through (0, 4)**

2. $x = y$ **a line with slope 1 that passes through (0, 0)**

3. $y = 5$ **a line with slope 0 that passes through (0, 5)**

4. $x^2 + (y - 2)^2 = 25$ **a circle with center (0, 2) and radius 5**

Describe the geometric figure whose locus in space satisfies each condition.

5. $(x + 2)^2 + (y - 3)^2 + z^2 = 64$
   a sphere with center (-2, 3, 0) and radius 8

6. $(x - 2)^2 (y + 3)^2 + (z - 1)^2 = 81$
   a sphere with center (2, -3, 1) and radius 9

Draw a diagram and describe the locus of points.

7. all points in a plane that are 3 inches from a given segment and equidistant from the two endpoints **two points on the perpendicular bisector of the segment, one on each side, whose perpendicular distance to the segment is 3 in.**

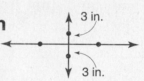

8. all points in a plane that are 3 inches from a given line and 3 inches from a given point on the line **two points, one on each side of the given point on the line, whose perpendicular distance from the point is 3 in.**

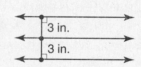

9. all points in a plane that are equidistant from the vertices of a given square **the center of the square; the point of intersection of the diagonals of the square**

10. all points in a plane that are 5 centimeters from a given point A and equidistant from points A and B that are 8 centimeters apart **two points, the intersection of the perpendicular bisector of $\overline{AB}$ and the circle with center A and radius 5**

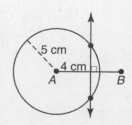

NAME _____ DATE _____

Practice

Mappings

Each figure below has a preimage or is the image of isometry.
Write the image of each given preimage listed in Exercise 1–6.

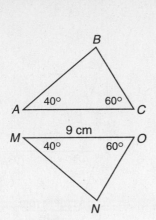

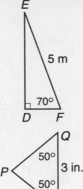

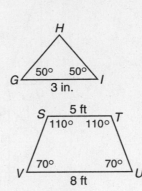

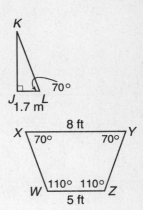

1. △ABC

2. △DEF

3. △GHI

4. △ONM

5. Quadrilateral STUV

6. Quadrilateral XYZW

7. Make a Table   Benjamin has seven employees who work in his store: Janell, Pedro, David, Elyse, Faye, Gordon, and Irene. Janell and Gordon work full time, 5 days in a row per week. Pedro and Faye each work 4 days per week. Pedro cannot work on Thursdays. David and Elyse also work 4 days per week each. David cannot work on weekends, and Elyse cannot work on Wednesdays. Irene works any three days assigned each week. Benjamin needs three people to work on Monday through Thursday, five to work on Friday, and six to work on weekends. Make a possible schedule for Benjamin to use.

Geometry

Practice

Mappings

Each figure below has a preimage or is the image of isometry.
Write the image of each given preimage listed in Exercise 1–6.

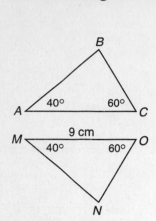

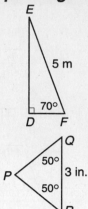

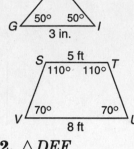

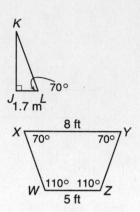

1. △ABC
   △MNO

2. △DEF
   △JKL

3. △GHI
   △RPQ or △QPR

4. △ONM
   △CBA

5. Quadrilateral STUV
   quadrilateral ZWXY or
   quadrilateral WZYX

6. Quadrilateral XYZW
   quadrilateral UVST or
   quadrilateral VUTS

7. **Make a Table** Benjamin has seven employees who work in
   his store: Janell, Pedro, David, Elyse, Faye, Gordon, and Irene.
   Janell and Gordon work full time, 5 days in a row per week.
   Pedro and Faye each work 4 days per week. Pedro cannot work
   on Thursdays. David and Elyse also work 4 days per week
   each. David cannot work on weekends, and Elyse cannot work
   on Wednesdays. Irene works any three days assigned each
   week. Benjamin needs three people to work on Monday
   through Thursday, five to work on Friday, and six to work on
   weekends. Make a possible schedule for Benjamin to use.
   Possible answer:

	M	T	W	T	F	S	S
Janell	X	X	X			X	X
Pedro	X				X	X	X
David		X	X	X	X		
Elyse				X	X	X	X
Faye				X	X	X	X
Gordon	X	X	X			X	X
Irene					X	X	X

Geometry

Practice

Reflections

For the figure at the right, name the reflection image of each of the following over line ℓ.

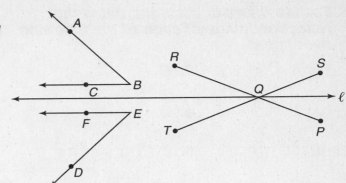

1. A   2. C

3. T   4. Q

4. $\overline{BC}$ 6. $\angle CBA$

5. $\overline{PR}$ 8. $\overline{QT}$

For each figure, indicate if the figure has <u>line symmetry</u>, <u>point symmetry</u>, or <u>both</u>.

9.
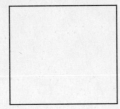

10.

11.
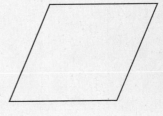

Use a straightedge to draw the reflection image of each figure over line *m*.

12.
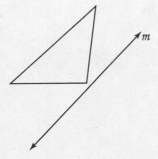

13.
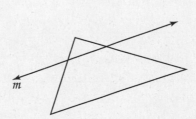

14.

Draw all possible lines of symmetry. If none exist, write <u>none</u>.

15.

16.

17.

Geometry

NAME _____ DATE _____

Practice

Reflections

For the figure at the right, name the
reflection image of each of the following
over line ℓ.

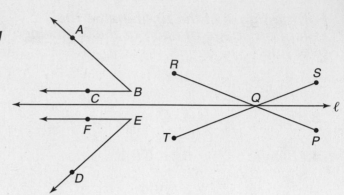

1. A **D**   2. C **F**

3. T **R**   4. Q **Q**

4. $\overline{BC}$ **$\overline{EF}$**   6. ∠CBA **∠FED**

5. $\overline{PR}$ **$\overline{ST}$**   8. $\overline{QT}$ **$\overline{QR}$**

For each figure, indicate if the figure has <u>line symmetry</u>, <u>point
symmetry</u>, or <u>both</u>.

9.    10.    11.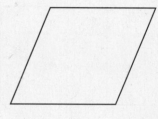

    both   **line**   **point**

Use a straightedge to draw the reflection image of each figure
over line m.

12. 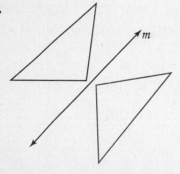   13. 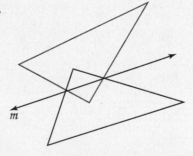   14.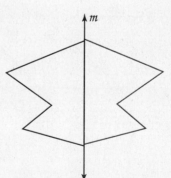

Draw all possible lines of symmetry. If none exist, write <u>none</u>.

15. 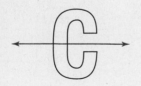   16. 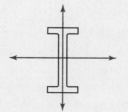   17.

                                                  none

Translations

For each of the following, lines ℓ and m are parallel. Determine whether Figure 3 is a translation image of Figure 1. Write <u>yes</u> or <u>no</u>. Explain your answer.

1.

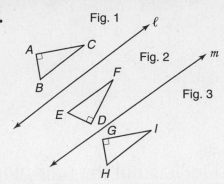

2.

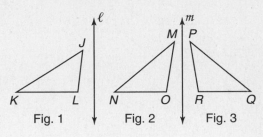

3.

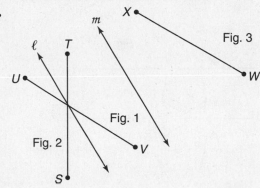

4.

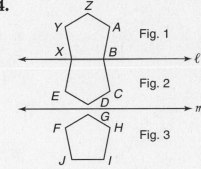

For Exercises 5–8, refer to the figures above.

5. Name the reflection of $\overline{ST}$ with respect to line ℓ. If none is drawn, write *none*.

6. Name the reflection of $\triangle JKL$ with respect to line ℓ. If none is drawn, write *none*.

7. Name the reflection of pentagon *XYZAB* with respect to line ℓ. If none is drawn, write *none*.

8. Name the reflection of $\overline{UV}$ with respect to line *m*. If none is drawn, write *none*.

Find the translation image of each geometric figure with respect to the parallel lines ℓ and *m*.

9.

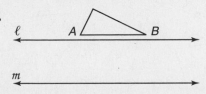

10.

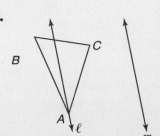

NAME_____ DATE _____

Practice

Translations

For each of the following, lines ℓ and m are parallel. Determine whether Figure 3 is a translation image of Figure 1. Write _yes_ or _no_. Explain your answer.

1.

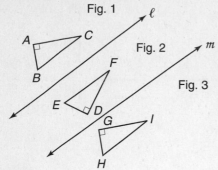

yes

2.

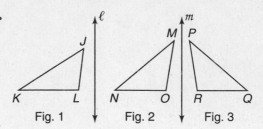

No; Fig. 2 is not the reflection of Fig. 1 with respect to ℓ.

3.

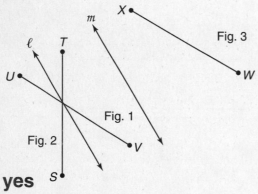

yes

4.

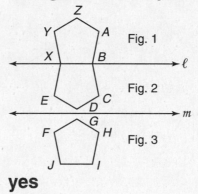

yes

For Exercises 5–8, refer to the figures above.

5. Name the reflection of $\overline{ST}$ with respect to line ℓ. If none is drawn, write _none_. **VU**

6. Name the reflection of △JKL with respect to line ℓ. If none is drawn, write _none_. **none**

7. Name the reflection of pentagon XYZAB with respect to line ℓ. If none is drawn, write _none_. **pentagon XEDCB**

8. Name the reflection of $\overline{UV}$ with respect to line m. If none is drawn, write _none_. **none**

Find the translation image of each geometric figure with respect to the parallel lines ℓ and m.

9.

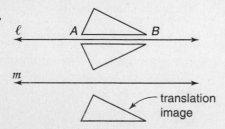

translation image

10.

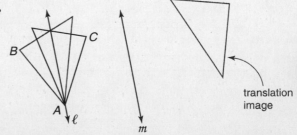

translation image

Geometry

Practice

Rotations

Two lines intersect to form an angle with the following measure. Find the angle of rotation for each.

1. 40°

2. 72°

3. 23°

4. 35°

5. 55°

6. 63°

Use the angle of rotation to find the rotation image with respect to lines s and t.

7.

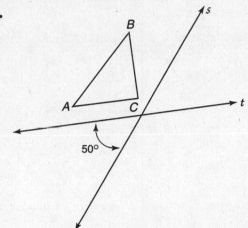

8.

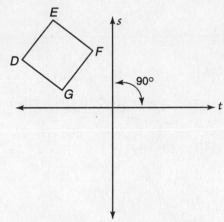

9.

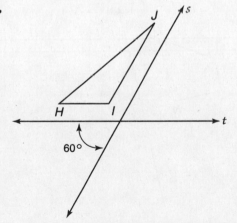

10.

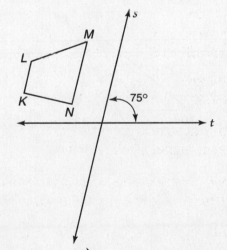

11.

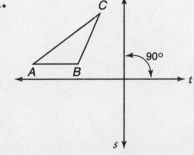

12.

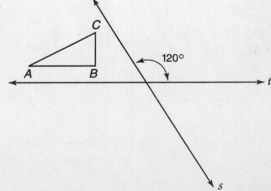

Geometry

Rotations

Two lines intersect to form an angle with the following measure. Find the angle of rotation for each.

1. 40° **80°**

2. 72° **144°**

3. 23° **46°**

4. 35° **70°**

5. 55° **110°**

6. 63° **126°**

Use the angle of rotation to find the rotation image with respect to lines s and t.

7.

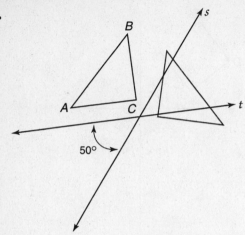

8.

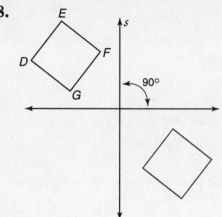

9.

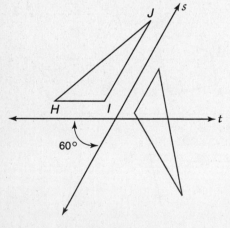

10.

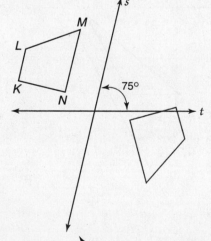

11.

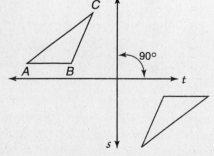

12.

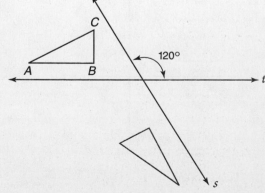

NAME_____ DATE _____

Practice

Student Edition
Pages 746–753

Dilations

A dilation with center C and a scale factor k maps X onto Y. Find |k| for each dilation. Then determine whether each dilation is an enlargement, a reduction, or a congruence transformation.

1. $CY = 15, CX = 10$

2. $CY = 2, CX = 2$

3. $CX = 5, CY = 2$

4. $CY = 20, CX = \frac{1}{2}$

Find the measure of the dilation image of $\overline{AB}$ with the given scale factor.

5. $AB = 6$ in., $k = -\frac{2}{3}$

6. $AB = 4$ in., $k = 1$

7. $AB = 1\frac{1}{2}$ in., $k = \frac{1}{2}$

8. $AB = 20$ in., $k = -2\frac{1}{2}$

Find each scale factor, find the image of A with respect to a dilation with center C.

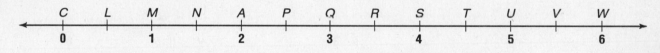

9. 3

10. $\frac{1}{4}$

11. $2\frac{1}{4}$

12. $\frac{3}{4}$

Graph each set of ordered pairs. Then connect the points in order. Using (0, 0) as the center of dilation and a scale factor of 2, draw the dilation image. Repeat this using a scale factor of $\frac{1}{2}$.

13. (2, 2), (4, 6), (6, −2)

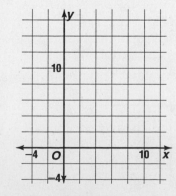

14. (0, 2), (−4, 2), (−4, −2)

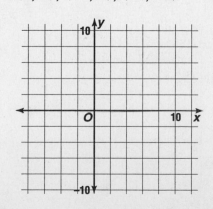

Practice

Dilations

A dilation with center C and a scale factor k maps X onto Y. Find $|k|$ for each dilation. Then determine whether each dilation is an enlargement, a reduction, or a congruence transformation.

1. $CY = 15$, $CX = 10$ $\frac{3}{2}$; **enlargement**

2. $CY = 2$, $CX = 2$ **1; congruence**

3. $CX = 5$, $CY = 2$ $\frac{2}{5}$; **reduction**

4. $CY = 20$, $CX = \frac{1}{2}$ **40; enlargement**

Find the measure of the dilation image of $\overline{AB}$ with the given scale factor.

5. $AB = 6$ in., $k = -\frac{2}{3}$ **4 in.**

6. $AB = 4$ in., $k = 1$ **4 in.**

7. $AB = 1\frac{1}{2}$ in., $k = \frac{1}{2}$ **$\frac{3}{4}$ in.**

8. $AB = 20$ in., $k = -2\frac{1}{2}$ **50 in.**

Find each scale factor, find the image of A with respect to a dilation with center C.

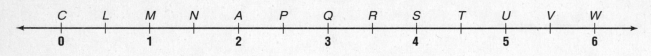

9. 3 **W**

10. $\frac{1}{4}$ **L**

11. $2\frac{1}{4}$ **T**

12. $\frac{3}{4}$ **N**

Graph each set of ordered pairs. Then connect the points in order. Using (0, 0) as the center of dilation and a scale factor of 2, draw the dilation image. Repeat this using a scale factor of $\frac{1}{2}$.

13. (2, 2), (4, 6), (6, −2)

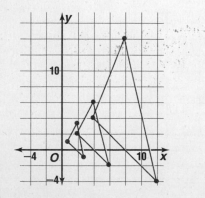

14. (0, 2), (−4, 2), (−4, −2)

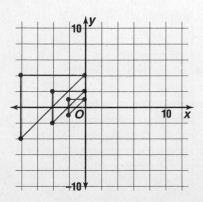

Horizons Academic Center
6104 Westline Drive
Houston, TX 77036
(713) 988-0007